Mother&Baby Book

Your guide to happy babies and toddlers

By Shaaron Biddulph
with Steve Biddulph

LEOPARD

Contents

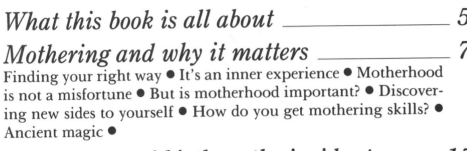

The preschool year _____ 91

Questions and answers. A group of parents share problems and solutions ● Likeability ● How to help a child speak pleasantly ● Preparing for school ●

Index _____ 109

Activity boxes

Am I ready to be a mother? 17 ● The mixed feelings exercise 18 ● Pregnancy diary 21 ● Getting ready for bonding 22 ● Delight in music 23 ● Navel gazing 27 ● Baby massage 33 ● Quick and simple meals 34 ● Recharge your own battery 35 ● Reducing the risk of sudden infant death syndrome 37 ● Sterilising feeding equipment 42 ● Happy snaps 44 ● Teaching co-operation 46 ● Beautiful baby 47 ● Disappearing games 49 ● How to fold a nappy 51 ● Tickle games 55 ● Birthday letters 61 ● Feelings and faces 65 ● Making a special play space 69 ● The mother turtle game 70 ● Imagination and exercise games 74 ● The sensuous child 75 ● Quiet time 76 ● Fun with numbers 77 ● Essential materials 79 ● Tests of strength 83 ● A restful environment 85 ● Stop on command 86 ● Animals and feelings 87 ● Reading preparation 88 ● Protecting children from sexual abuse 89 ● Gifts of power 93 ● Thinking games 94 ● Doing the dishes 96 ● Signifying changes 97 ● Stimulating the imagination 100 ● Memory improvement 101 ● Enjoying visits to the doctor and dentist 104 ● Helping to build motor skills 105 ● Harmony and happiness 106 ●

A NOTE ABOUT HE, SHE AND THEM

Once upon a time, childrearing books referred to all children as 'he' (as if little girls didn't matter). Then books started using 'he or she', which was awkward, or alternating 'he' and 'she', which meant they were wrong 50 per cent of the time. We think the English language needs improving, so have written the book the way people speak — such as, 'if your baby cries, you can pick them up and comfort them'. In other words, 'them' is used as a singular pronoun. We wanted to let you know that we are reforming the language and not just using bad grammar. We hope this makes for smooth reading.

What this book is all about

A popular women's magazine, which I often read, has a page in which women write about their problems and other readers suggest solutions. One letter really caught my eye as it was so easy to identify with. A young mother called Clara, with three small children, wrote that she had lost the ability to have fun. She felt isolated, inadequate and angry, and was starting to hate being a parent. She 'knew it was supposed to be better than this' and wanted help.

The replies from mothers around the country showed they understood well how Clara was feeling. One mother, also with three children, guessed that Clara could be caught in a vicious circle, hating herself for her angry outbursts, feeling guilty, not living up to her own high standards. She knew this feeling because she had 'been there'. She had solved the problem by changing her attitude, becoming kind and gentle to herself. To her surprise, she found that this kindness and tolerance passed itself on to the children. Perhaps, she wondered, this could work for Clara, too?

Other women suggested making time to have more fun with the children, and relaxing her high expectations. They reminded Clara of the need to have breaks for herself. Others suggested taking Vitamin B for stress, playing a sport and so on. These were practical, 'road-tested' ideas, offered respectfully, with a large dose of understanding and encouragement thrown in. It was as if a caring group of down-to-earth mothers was physically gathering around Clara to bear her up and give her strength. No doctor, journalist, researcher, child-development lecturer or any kind of expert could give this type of help. These were women who *had lived through* what they were talking about.

To succeed in their chosen purpose, mothers need help from other mothers. (And fathers from other fathers.) That's the kind of book this is — non-expert, conveying support and suggestions from parent to parent. Everything in it has been gleaned from parents' experience, some recent and some going back generations. The aim is to make you feel surrounded by friends who respect your judgment, but can offer vast experience and helpful clues for raising your children.

The book has seven sections, which cover roughly the phases that little children pass through:

1. Mothering and why it matters (getting it all in perspective).
2. Pregnancy and birth (before pregnancy, during pregnancy and up to the birth).
3. Babe in arms (making contact, taking care of them and you).
4. The mobile baby (exploring and communicating).
5. Toddlers 2–4 (discipline, love and learning).
6. Fathers (what they do for children and mothers).
7. The preschool year (getting ready for the world).

And there's a bonus — almost a second book in the first one. In each section, we have included special Activity Boxes. These are like recipes from which you can pick and choose. They give specific activities you can enjoy with your child at that exact stage of development. Often, these activities are the most fun parts of parenting and the parts which will give you special satisfaction.

Maaron Biddulph

Position Vacant. Mother required. Hours: 24 hours per day on call, reducing to just on call after 18 years. Skills: organizational skills, intelligence, compassion, dedication, stamina, assertiveness and sense of humour. Low status, no sick leave. Salary: none.

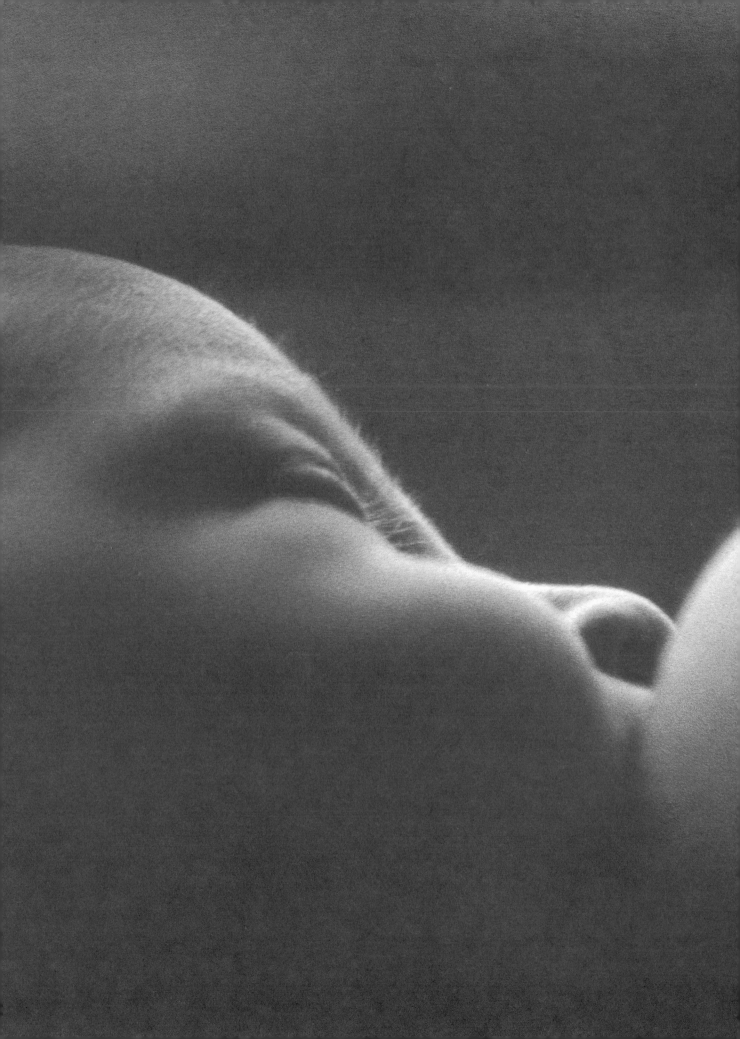

Mothering and why it matters

Finding your *right way*

Before we get into the midst of the baby action, let's talk about motherhood itself. There is much conflicting advice about being a mother and many myths, some of which can hurt us.

As you imagine (or remember) holding your newborn baby in your arms, carefully, tenderly, are you aware of a slight surge in your heartbeat? You feel at the same time very privileged and very responsible. You ask yourself, 'Will I be a good enough mother? Will I get it right?'

A million decisions face us from the moment of conception. 'Should I have a homebirth or is that irresponsible?' And when the baby is born: 'Should I ignore their cries at night?' And in the toddler years: 'Should I stay out of the workforce until the children are of school age?'

It's quite funny, when you think about it. There are records of human existence going back 700,000 years, but no one has yet found in a cave the tablets of stone or ancient parchments with the answers. If there were right answers to these questions, you'd think they would have been discovered by now!

The truth is, *there are no right answers.* Parenting is a personal journey and no one else can tell your way to do it. You and your child are a unique combination and you have to find out what works best for both of you. And each child you have is different too! Searching for and finding *your* way will give you growing strength and confidence, interspersed with times of soul-searching. The important thing is, you aren't measuring up to someone else's prescription; you're just being real... So what is *real* motherhood about?

IT'S AN INNER EXPERIENCE

Motherhood brings with it some remarkable experiences. You'll know what it's like to lie quietly in bed, looking at your baby's face and feeling your heart melt with a sweet, aching love which is beyond words. You'll also know what it's like to:

● Change 6800 nappies.
● Cook and clean up 15,000 meals.
● Wipe countless snotty noses.
● Sit for two months of your life in doctors' waiting rooms; and somehow enjoy it!

The *inner* experience of motherhood subtly and gradually tells you what to do. There is an in-built guidance system which comes from two sources: from carefully listening to your own feelings and from paying attention to the signals sent out by your child.

It's all about trying things out. As you get on with the job, day by day, you will find that some things work and some don't. So you change. Some things work partially, but don't feel right, so you drop them. (Many parents feel this way about smacking children — it gets obedience, but at what price?) Often, of course, you can't tell what is right until you try. The point is, you decide.

PAT was a woman of about 60, cheerful and rosy-faced, with wisps of white hair escaping a bun and the look of someone who has just walked across English fields with spaniels. She told us in a group workshop that she had raised five children. Her husband, a doctor, had insisted they follow 'the book' which, in those days (the '40s), meant leaving children in a cot to cry and not cuddling or holding them for fear of spoiling. Pat went along with this, but when their fifth — a boy — was born, she told her husband, 'This one is mine — I'm going to spoil him!' She fed him in her bed, went to him when he cried, and cuddled and jiggled him on her knee as a toddler — all highly suspect practices in those days. 'And you know what?' she beamed. 'He's grown up to be the most well adjusted of them all.'

Parents usually do things their own way, given the chance. A good friend of ours slept with her baby daughter for the first three years, fearful about her restlessness and troubled breathing. People advised her not to, as it tired her out, and doctors told her there was nothing wrong with the child. All she knew was that she couldn't let her baby sleep alone and that something else was not right. Eventually, at six, her daughter was diagnosed with very enlarged adenoids. She had them removed and was immediately able to sleep soundly, and gained weight, health and vitality.

Toilet training features high on experts' lists and parents' concerns. One mother had no idea how to approach toilet training. She had only

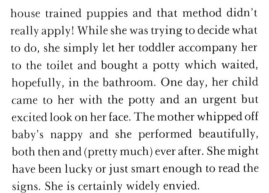

house trained puppies and that method didn't really apply! While she was trying to decide what to do, she simply let her toddler accompany her to the toilet and bought a potty which waited, hopefully, in the bathroom. One day, her child came to her with the potty and an urgent but excited look on her face. The mother whipped off baby's nappy and she performed beautifully, both then and (pretty much) ever after. She might have been lucky or just smart enough to read the signs. She is certainly widely envied.

The same advice will work for one person and not another. Listen to other people, but make up your own mind. Have a go and change tack if it doesn't work. Children are programmed to grow up anyway and parenthood is meant to succeed (or no one would do it again). It may be the first time in your life that you listen to your *own* judgment and go with it. It's a feeling that grows on you.

MOTHERHOOD IS NOT A MISFORTUNE

There has been a lot of brainwashing about motherhood and it still goes on. From the '40s and '50s, we had the image of the 'perfect mother' who lived for her family. Feminism has helped, but we've added other burdens by becoming Superwoman, who is everything — career woman, mother and sex symbol all rolled in together.

Isn't it interesting that we criticised our mothers (at least in our thoughts) for being doormats to the family? They criticise us for the opposite reason — for neglecting our children. They worry, too, that we will miss out on the special early years of family life — that we will be unfulfilled. It's a paradox — the independence and confidence we enjoy grew from their stability and the investment they made in us. In quiet moments, we sit and wonder: is it possible to have freedom *and* be a fulfilled family person? It's clearly time for a new balance to be found.

In some ways, we women have almost been conned out of our heritage. In a media world, where success is materially based, a kind of social pressure has developed, to see motherhood as a secondary part of life, almost a misfortune. It's as if having kids is a handicap in the race to succeed. This is not the view of the mothers who contributed to this book. We maintain, with passionate feeling, that parenthood is certainly tough but, taken overall, it is wonderful to have and to raise children. It is a blessing.

BUT IS MOTHERHOOD IMPORTANT?

It's *very important*. Sometimes people say: 'I'm just a mother' or get asked by people with no brains: 'Do you work?' Raising kids, even as far as school age, is more significant, in terms of affecting the lives of other human beings, than anything else most of us will ever do. How you raise your children will affect all their relationships. The qualities they possess, or lack, will affect all the people they ever meet, learn from and work with, and more so those they love and live with, and the children they raise, and their children, forever after.

Motherhood isn't the whole of your life, but it's a huge part of it. For up to 18 years, children are a daily concern — longer, if you can't get them to leave home! You can be overawed by this feeling of something so big coming into your life. Quite a lot of us panic.

But you can't change the fact that you're a mother. It's like in the kids' game of chasey: *you're it*. This child has got you for better or for worse. You start to assess yourself, not always favourably. Through the years, as your child grows up, comparisons will always be there to make. Their teacher might be more creative.

Their grandma might be more indulgent. The neighbour will be better at making clothes. Their friend's mother will be more fashionable. At least, that's how it could look. But none of these people has the central role. You are *Mum*.

In responding to your new status, you have a choice. Your mothering can either be passive, coping, just reacting to one thing after another; or it can be active, conscious and with definite aims (modified as you learn from experience). The difference is that with *conscious parenting* you know it's a job, you want to do it well, and you gather the resources and help you need. You give it your best shot. You take it on wholeheartedly and with determined creativity. If you do this, a very interesting thing happens — you start to *stretch*.

Vivien was 28 when she gave birth to twins. She insisted on breastfeeding them, even though many people argued the advantages of bottlefeeding.

As she told us, 'I've always been a shy person. I'd never dreamed of standing up to anyone in authority. I said "no" to a nurse who offered my babies some milk formula, then I got quite cross with a doctor who behaved patronisingly and finally I blew up my mother who seemed to think I would be hopeless. Now she is treating me with new respect. I'm treating myself with new respect.'

Parenthood will definitely make you more assertive. It can even help to heal hurts which have come down through many generations.

Margaret was a trained nurse who had left work to be a parent. She loved her two children dearly, but found it hard to show affection. When she watched other mothers hugging and smooching their babies and toddlers, Marg felt awkward and tense, as she could not do this with her own children. After talking with a close friend, she realised that she could not remember ever being held or comforted by her mother.

As she recalled the loneliness of her childhood, she began finding it easier to be close to her kids and her husband. It didn't happen overnight, and took some courage, as she softened her tough outer shell and got in touch with how lonely she often really felt. But, as her capacity for closeness slowly increased, she felt happier than ever before. As a bonus, her kids were noticeably healthier and had fewer behavioural problems than previously, and her marriage grew stronger.

Many adults have felt huge 'gaps' in their own training or preparedness for life. Many skills and qualities — like warmth, humour, toughness,

A loving child is a child who has experienced love. A compassionate child has experienced somebody who cared about their feelings and needs. But it goes both ways — our children can *teach us* to love, laugh, have fun, slow down, be versatile. They can show us how to be here in this present moment to experience the laughter or tears — to be fully alive.

friendliness — need to be learned as concretely as learning to read or ride a bike. Sometimes we only learn these things in our 20s or 30s, prompted by the wish to pass them on to our kids.

It isn't *all* up to you. You and your child are two souls meeting. You bring your background, life experiences and imperfections, and your child brings their unique disposition, health, handicaps and talents. Your partner, your other children, friends, family and community all add to the melting pot of experience.

Your kids may not learn to be loving unless you show them love and encourage them. They may not learn to solve problems unless you help them to think clearly and to understand their feelings. You have the chance to make them healthy, as you teach them to like good food and take joy in using their bodies actively. Loving, alert, healthy children don't just happen. The seed is there — children love to love, they love to explore, learn, eat, exercise, be creative. But these things need to be drawn out, nurtured and taught. You have the opportunity to make a lot of difference in these key parts of their life.

Very few of us feel equipped to be a parent. Becoming one impels us to learn. If we don't have the necessary qualities yet, we can learn

them and other people can help us. Then we can pass them on to our children.

Annie, a 19-year-old single mother, was having a lot of trouble with her strong-willed toddler. However, one of her friends showed skill in disciplining Max whenever they visited her house. Annie was embarrassed at first, but took note of the way her friend was definite, kindly, but strong and persistent until Max co-operated. Annie also noticed how much Max loved to visit her friend. She started to use the same tone and approach that her friend had unknowingly shown her. And it began to work.

Sue, 32, a hairdresser from Scotland, started a playgroup to get to know local young mothers, as she had no relatives nearby. 'I was shy, but I was going up the wall at home,' she told us. 'I didn't know how to talk to people. I would see other mothers at the Health Centre and not know how to start. In the end, I just went up to people and said: "Hello, I'm Sue, what's your name?" and we got talking. Now my son Angus does the same thing with the kids in the playgroup. There's no way he'll be shy like I was.'

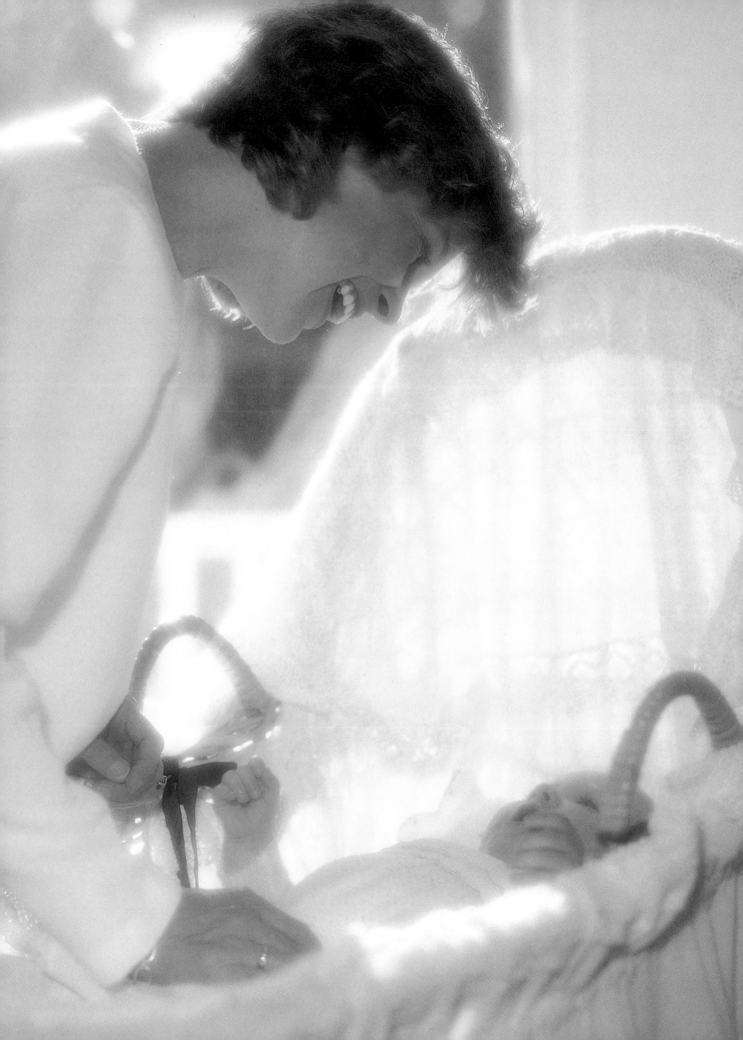

Discovering new sides to yourself

Parenthood invites you — even forces you — to extend yourself in ways you didn't think possible. You will get better at making friends, simply because you need them. You will also be showing your toddler about friendliness. This will make it easier for them when they get to school. Parenthood will certainly stretch your relationship with your partner, learning from each other, leaning on each other, and fighting with each other as you parent together.

By now, we hope you have gathered that a real mother is never perfect, no one ever 'arrives'. This is good because a perfect mother would be a pain. She would be of no use to kids because they would have nothing to offer in return and there would be none of the learning on the hoof that makes human beings vulnerable and, therefore, loveable. A real mother is *better* than a perfect mother. Believe it.

HOW DO YOU GET MOTHERING SKILLS?

Any way you can! But there are three main sources:

1. Recall them from your own childhood. The easiest way is to have been mothered well yourself. If you had a mother who knew how to love and raise children, while being a 'real' human being in bad times as well as good, you have a head start. She will probably also have had her own life, interests and talents. These may have been put on a back burner for a while with babies and toddlers around, but they were not lost and came back strongly at the earliest opportunity. She will have shown you that she was **herself** first. And a partner, and a mother. She made sacrifices and accepted delays in her life, but didn't lose herself in order to raise her children. You had a feeling she was doing what she wanted. If you were lucky enough to have had a mother like that, appreciate it.

2. Acquire them later by finding people who can fill the gaps. Often, you can find good models to copy. Perhaps when you were little your father was the one who taught you certain qualities, such as having fun, being strong and independent, the importance of laughter. You may want to incorporate his qualities into your mothering. Perhaps a grandma, aunt or friendly neighbour was often more affirming than your parents could be. A teacher might have believed in you and your potential. Even now, you may find that certain people attract you because they 'have it together' in ways you admire. Spend time with them, enjoy their company and soak up the qualities they show. In this way, you keep on 'growing yourself up'.

3. Learn by experience and experimentation. Teach yourself. We all know people who have just figured things out for themselves; this is one of the inspiring things about human beings. You can do it, too. Note the aspects of mothering where you feel you are on shaky ground and decide to work systematically on these areas.

- Ask other mothers.
- Ask a health visitor.
- Ask a counsellor.
- Read books.
- Read magazines.
- Watch television programmes.
- Watch what others do.

ANCIENT MAGIC

Motherhood is an ancient and powerful magic which shapes the world. There is an exquisite, powerful and healing connection between every mother and her child. Every caring action a mother takes, large or small, contributes to her own and her child's well-being. The 'special moments' with a child are really lovely, but it's also the routine times, the little corrections to behaviour, the assistance, explanations and comforts you give. The gentleness you show when you put on their shoes for the millionth time and the smile you give as you watch them walking towards you . . . these everyday things add up to help your child to grow into a fully alive, loving and capable adult.

This is the big view, something to remember when you can't see the wood for the trees (or the child for the nappies!). What you are doing is *very* important. It's as simple as that.

The two of you make a unique combination. Remember to listen to what *you* think as well as what others suggest. You will be learning all the time and your confidence will grow.

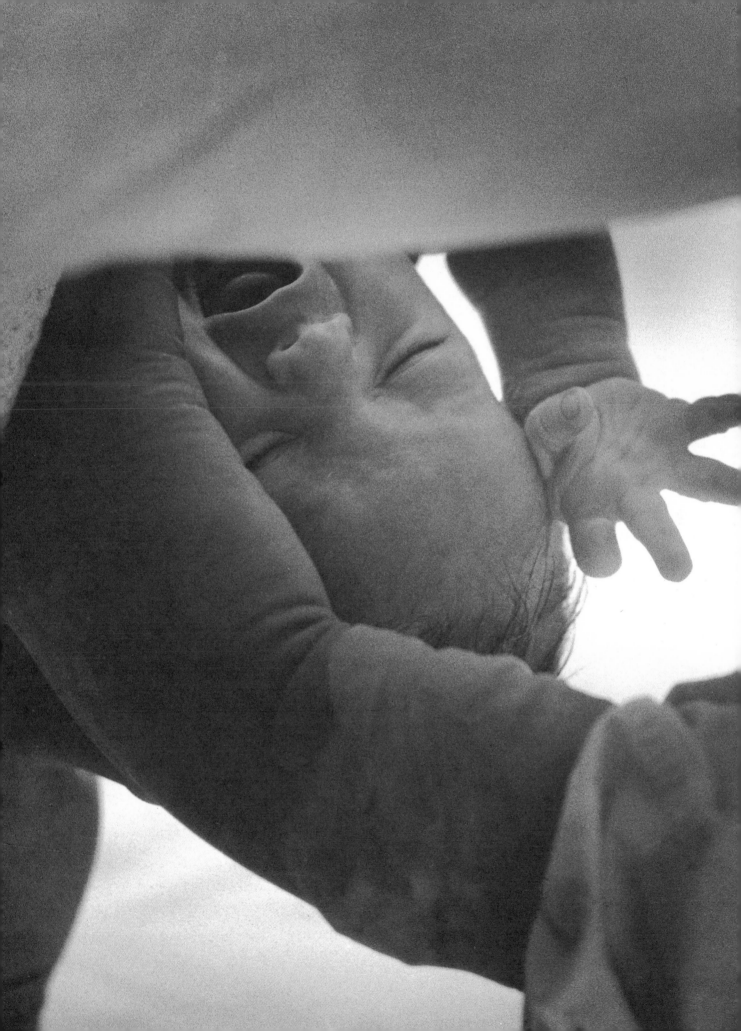

Pregnancy and birth
— the inside story

Before conception

SHOULD WE HAVE A BABY?

It may seem strange, in a book on mothering, to appear to be talking you *out* of having a baby. But that is not our intention. Our intention is to encourage you to weigh up the pros and cons and get clearer in your mind about this important choice.

Every time you make love, there is a chance you will become pregnant and have a baby. It is quite possible for a woman to have from 10 to 20 babies in the course of an (exhausting) lifetime. The fact that so few people have this many means that lots of us exercise some choice.

No contraceptive method is 100 per cent foolproof. Nevertheless, contraceptive methods allow most of us the privilege of timing when, and if, we conceive a child. Perhaps this is our first real responsibility in motherhood — the timing of our pregnancy.

There are times in anyone's life when to become pregnant would be a real crisis. Let's say

To have or not to have — a life changing decision. Talk together about what each of you thinks and feels. Work towards being clear within yourself and with each other. This is a life-long commitment. Are you willing individually *and* together to take it on?

you were really sick, having huge fights with your partner, there was trouble with in-laws, your mother had just died or you already had three children under three and one of them had a heart condition requiring expensive care... The bank was about to repossess the house and the weather forecast was for gales! Perhaps this would be a good time not to become pregnant!

However, we often hear of people who *do* conceive a child in the midst of a traumatic time — the loss of a grandparent, for instance. There is a miraculous quality to this, which reminds us that there is always new life coming along to replace the old.

Sometimes parents recall that a certain child was conceived at a seemingly bad time and things turned out perfectly in the long run. That's great. But, since we have a lot more choice in the matter than our mothers' generation did, we may as well make good use of this.

WHAT IF YOU ARE FEELING AMBIVALENT?

Is this you? Sometimes you feel you would give anything to have a baby. Then the next day you are so aware of the pleasure of being free and able to go out to dinner or a movie, and stay out late without having to worry about childcare problems. Then you see a mother with a gorgeous baby or a cute, loving toddler and you want one, too. Then you see someone struggling with a screaming, angry, bratty kid and you think, 'Thank God that's not me.'

Am I ready to be a mother?

Are you thinking of having a baby, but unsure if this is the right time? Following is a (half-serious) look at the factors you have to consider. Tick the boxes you feel relate most closely to your situation, choosing at least one in each category.

Your career or education

1. This is a good time in my career/education to have a child. ( )
2. Having a baby now would interrupt my education. ( )
3. Having a baby now would affect my career. ( )
4. I'm more interested in having a baby — my job/education are not that important right now. ( )

Can you and your partner afford a baby?

1. Yes, we can afford a baby without any real problems. ( )
2. Starting a family would be a whole lot easier, financially, in a couple of years' time. ( )
3. I'm not sure if we can live on one income or on benefits. What do babies cost anyway? ( )
4. It doesn't make a lot of difference — we're broke all the time anyway. ( )

Your age

1. I want to have a baby while I am young. ( )
2. I am older (a whole 22!) and want to have a baby now. ( )
3. I am young and there are things I want to do before being tied down with a baby. ( )
4. I *am* older (38) and want to have a baby now. ( )

Your relationship

1. I have a really strong and stable relationship with my partner. It has stood the test of time. ( )
2. Our relationship is pretty shaky. Maybe having children will help bring us closer. ( )

3. Our relationship is pretty shaky. Maybe we should give it a bit more time before we decide to have children. ( )
4. Relationship — who needs it? I'll find a sperm donor somewhere! ( )

Roles and expectations

1. My partner and I are clear about sharing the workload. He is good with kids and wants them as much as I do. ( )
2. My partner is unsure — he doesn't seem very keen. He's even jealous of the canary. ( )
3. My partner says, sure, we can have kids, as long as I look after them and they don't touch the stereo. ( )

Your health

1. I've already started eliminating toxins from my system, quit smoking, stopped drinking alcohol or taking drugs, and am using another method of contraception for six months or so to clear the Pill from my system. I'm also eating a lot of fresh vegetables, salads, fruit and grains. ( )
2. Some of the above. ( )
3. None of the above. ( )
4. My partner is doing the same and also staying away from agricultural chemicals, industrial pollutants, petrochemicals and high-voltage installations. ( )
5. My partner says there's nothing wrong with his sperm; what am I talking about? ( )

Your fitness

1. I've always been fit and have started a gentle exercise program which will continue during pregnancy. ( )
2. I'll start tomorrow. ( )
3. I'm looking forward to being pregnant — watching videos, being waited on and eating what I feel like. ( )

Look at the numbers you've ticked. If you have nine in the 1 category, you're probably already pregnant. If you have nine 3s, it would be better to think again!

The mixed-feelings exercise

Whenever you are in two minds about a decision in your life, this is telling you something important. Don't just toss a coin or rush into one of the two options. You must never ignore mixed feelings which often indicate that you are in a transition time, a time when you are gradually changing from one stage of life to another. It's important to respect this process and go very slowly.

The secret of navigating through a transition time is to take small steps and explore each aspect of the dilemma. For example, on a day when you are feeling really clucky and wishing you had a baby, do something small but symbolic, as if you were already pregnant. Perhaps you could:

- Browse in a baby shop.
- Think of names you like and make a list.
- Buy some booties.
- Plan a space in your bedroom where you could put a cot.

Then, on a day when you are thinking, 'No, maybe it's best I don't have a child right now' do something small but symbolic, as if you were *not* going to become pregnant:

- Go to the beach by yourself.
- Dress up and go out to have afternoon tea in a really elegant place.
- Have a long morning bath.

When you continue to express each side of your ambivalence in this way, it allows for a natural decision to occur. Over a few weeks or even a month or two, it will become evident that you are having many more days of wanting a baby and less of wanting to be independent, or vice versa.

All big decisions are probably best made this way, since they allow us to explore our feelings unconsciously, until we know in our bones that we are doing what we really want. Wiser and older cultures than ours knew how to *feel* their way into a decision and were not so hung up about being logical or consistent. Logic matters, but your heart must be in on a decision for it to work.

What can you do when you have these swings in your feelings? Perhaps you could try some of the activities in the Activity Box at left — The Mixed-Feelings Exercise was developed by social worker Elizabeth Mellor.

It is useful to share your feelings with your partner and explain what you are doing, so that he is not totally bewildered, especially if he is a logical kind of man who likes things cut and dried. You can help by indicating that your present feelings are temporary — for example: '*Today*, I feel like being the mother of five kids!' or: '*Right now*, I'm really happy there are just the two of us.'

I vividly recall being in labour with our first child and saying spontaneously: 'Let's not have a baby. I think I'd rather wait for a year or two.' When feelings are expressed like this, they are out and gone. If we suppress our reservations and think: 'Oh, I shouldn't feel like that', we can end up in a tangle of squashed emotions.

Even if you are definite about wanting a baby, talk about it with your partner, so you can express what it is you both actually envisage. Share your dreams (and fears) to discover where they overlap and which can come true for you. Talk about your hopes — the fun, the company of a little person, the challenges and intrigue (what will they be like?), the joys of them maturing into a toddler, school child, teenager and adult. Perhaps your enthusiasms will be for different stages. Each partner may want a child for different reasons. Sometimes a man is keen to have a child he can do things with, while the woman is yearning for a dependent babe.

Talk to your partner also about the negative possibilities — what if we have a baby who cries all the time, won't sleep, has feeding trouble or is sick? However small and niggling, or ridiculous and fanciful, these thoughts need airing.

Sometimes a man resists having a child because he fears being replaced in his partner's affections. Or a woman fears losing her attractiveness through birth and breastfeeding. Many of these misgivings are totally unfounded or, if true, can be dealt with.

Some parents have fears about a baby dying, being abnormal or very sick; or birth being difficult. Again, these concerns and their implications are best talked through, as we've found that they can actually affect a couple's fertility. Once they resolve these questions, couples sometimes conceive a child after trying desperately for years.

You can also seek more information — genetic counselling, advice about pregnancy at your age, more realistic information about handicaps and differences in children. By meeting and talking with parents of disabled children, for example, you may realise the preciousness of life in all its variations, and become more comfortable with the potential risks and joys of parenthood.

As a result of exploring your inner feelings, and those of your partner, you will grow a great deal. If you decide you want to go ahead and have a baby, it will be with a real inner peace. You'll be far less prone to postnatal blues or partnership struggles in the early years, because you have done the preparatory soul-straightening work. There will still be hard times, and good and bad surprises, but somehow on the inside you will be thinking: 'Yes, this is what we want to be doing.' A woman who knows what she wants, and why, is a powerful and beautiful being.

Conception to birth

RIDING THE WAVE

Pregnancy is a little like catching a wave. Once you've started, from the very second that new life is conceived inside you, powerful forces are unleashed to carry you through. You are still the one doing the steering, but there is a Wow! Whoosh! Look out! kind of quality to it all, as you ride the energies and instincts which are subtly or not-so-subtly coming to the fore.

Even before conception, once your mind and body are set on this course of action, things begin to happen. Many women feel a new and different kind of pleasure in their love-making. There is often a strong feeling of rightness, purpose, excitement and joy. Some feel more open-hearted and closer to their partner. Men will often delight in the woman's abandoned and passionate surrender, and be surprised as they start to appreciate the many unexpected benefits of parenthood.

UNPLANNED PREGNANCY

'But wait a minute,' you may be saying, 'what about accidental pregnancies? Or deliberate ones on the part of the woman or man, without their partner's agreement?' People do 'get' pregnant

YOO HOO! Yes, That's right! Down HERE!

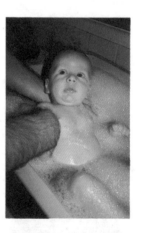

without discussion, or while pretending that they don't want a child and slipping up with contraception, or even actively tricking their partner. This simply means that the mixed feelings everyone feels have to be worked through during pregnancy or in the early years with the child. In fact, we know of couples having problems with their 20-year-old offspring, who are still arguing: 'See, I told you we should never have had kids!'

Joking aside, it is not fair to leave this kind of thing hanging around to get in the way of your relationship with your child or your partner. It takes two people to become pregnant. And since you now *have* a child, it's time to get on with caring for them.

CONCEPTION

Some women report knowing the exact moment they have conceived. Many others 'know' they are pregnant before any test has been done. (Tests available, without prescription, from a pharmacy can tell you within a few days.) How do you know? A combination of intuition and sensitivity to your body changes seems to help you notice the earliest stirrings of the new life inside you. Whether it has taken a long or short time for you to conceive, whether planned or not, feared or hoped for, the moment of confirmation of pregnancy is an awesome one, deserving of celebration. Go out and have a meal, (with a glass of mineral water!)

SHOCK!

Even if all the preamble has been positive, the momentousness of definitely being pregnant is still accompanied by just plain shock! Parents find themselves thinking: 'Not yet, I'm not ready' at the same time as — and perhaps because of — knowing they can't go back. Even the most longed-for, hoped-for and awaited pregnancy does not escape this 'Oh, my God' reaction.

Just because you are feeling this way, don't jump to the conclusion that you've made a terrible mistake. What you are really feeling is the ever-present truth which we usually choose to ignore — that nature or God or the power of the universe runs our lives and *we are never in complete control*. Perhaps the pregnancy is not as perfect as we had hoped or the timing is not quite right. But that is done now. We are on the roller coaster and it has just pulled out of the station. We can want what we want with all our hearts and plan thoroughly but, in the end, nature chooses.

So don't feel scared. Breathe a little more deeply and slowly, expand your spirit and feel what it really is — not fear, but *awe*. You are in on the creation of life.

This is the first and most important lesson of parenting. We provide the raw materials, make

Pregnancy diary

You can buy or make a daily diary for your pregnancy. This gives you the opportunity to jot down a little note about what you are experiencing, feeling and doing each day. For example, you might include visits to the doctor or midwife, questions you asked and answers received, and your feelings about them. Write down questions you would like answered. Important moments can be recorded — the pregnancy test, hearing the baby's heartbeat, the first kicks and so on.

This will make fascinating reading for your child in later years and is amazing to re-read, especially in subsequent pregnancies for comparison. In the blurry time of pregnancy, you will have kept precious memories to enjoy later. Writing a diary focuses you and gives you a sense of your personal growth, while measuring your progress towards the time of the birth.

our bodies, hearts and minds available, and wait for life to fill in the space when and as it will. Life will help us, if we teach ourselves to relax, to *let go*. This same lesson is repeated in pregnancy, birth, the child's growing years, adolescence, adulthood, and our own and our child's death.

FEARS

The early months of pregnancy can be vulnerable ones. It is helpful to notice, write down or talk about your sudden fears and worries, no matter how illogical or unpleasant they may seem to others. Seemingly out of nowhere, worries may arise about the unknown, your ability to handle the responsibilities of parenthood, fears for your children's future.

One way to understand these sweeping emotions is through the concept of 'recycling' which means that an experience you've had in the past,

Preparing your body (mind and spirit) even before conception gives you and your child the best of starts. You may also want to increase your physical stamina through safe exercise such as swimming and walking before and after conception.

Getting ready for bonding

suggested by Lindy Shillito

During pregnancy, you will find yourselves daydreaming and fantasising about what sort of child you will have. This is an important part of preparing yourself for your baby's arrival. You can try this now. In your imagination, think of your child and just let the answers come to you...

- Will you have a boy or a girl?
- What colour eyes and hair will the baby have?
- Will the baby be like you — in looks or personality?
- How will you all get along and where will this baby fit in with other children, existing or planned?
- How will your partner relate to the baby?
- What will you do together? How will your time be spent?
- What kind of things will you enjoy doing?
- Which parts will be hard and challenging?
- What will the child be like as a schoolchild, teenager, adult?
- What, especially, are you looking forward to?

These are some of the thoughts and questions which help to make a space in our lives, beginning the natural and vital process which is often called bonding or attachment. The reality may or may not match the fantasy, but it is good to prime your mind and heart by thinking in this way, and bringing unconscious hopes and dreams to the surface.

that is in some way incomplete, rises up again under similar circumstances. When you can recognise this, your unexpected feelings suddenly make more sense. For example...

Janet and Peter suffered a miscarriage of their first pregnancy. This is not a rare occurrence — as many as one in five pregnancies miscarry usually (but not always) in the early weeks or months. The emotional pain of miscarriage, for both partners, is often underestimated.

We'll let Janet tell, in her own words, how this affected her next pregnancy — how the feelings were being 'recycled': 'I knew in my rational part that things were going well, that there was no special need to worry. But I found, too, that I was highly alert to any signs of cramping, pain, stress, etc, which resembled that first pregnancy. A mild attack of cramp, when I was 14 weeks pregnant, came while I was at work. It passed without any consequence but, when I got home, I immediately was filled with memories of the night when I had lost my first baby, and I cried for a long time.

'While I had been sad at the time of the miscarriage, I guess there had been deeper sadness which I hadn't allowed myself to feel. Now that was pouring out of me. Afterwards, I felt fresher, more whole, and less afraid to love this baby, without holding back.' Janet's daughter was born a healthy 8 lb 13 oz (4 kg). It was very important for Janet to have allowed her heart to heal.

Marina, 27, did not get to the point of healing until she was in labour, in hospital. The birth was not proceeding properly and there was a lull while the staff considered what to do. An understanding nurse took a moment or two to talk with Marina about her feelings and thoughts. All at once, Marina began to sob and repeat something about 'I don't want to lose it'.

Rather than jump to conclusions and offer pat reassurances, the nurse asked: 'How could you lose it?' Marina suddenly experienced a wave of the most heart-rending distress. As her tears eased, she told the nurse about being pregnant at 14, the result of sexual assault by a relative. At birth, the baby had been taken from her and given up for adoption, never seen or touched by Marina. She had put the experience out of her mind, as much as she could, but now the pain of that old loss was preventing her from releasing this baby into the world.

She and the nurse spent some more time talking, then the nurse gave Marina a clear commitment that *this* baby would not be taken away. In a short time, her contractions began strongly again and she gave birth to a 6 lb 3 oz (3.2 kg) boy who was immediately placed in her joyful arms. There were few dry eyes in the birthing suite on that particular night.

In the past, many professionals, partners and other family members have simply glossed over these types of fears as being hormonal. 'Yes, women do get rather emotional when they are pregnant,' they say. True enough, but not without reason. You may begin to realise that this is a wonderful chance to clear out the cobwebs of the past and so become fully present now. Previous experiences which can be recycled and healed in pregnancy include:

● Terminations (abortions) that a woman may have undergone voluntarily or had imposed on her as a young girl.

● Earlier births which had been difficult or mishandled.

● Caesareans.

● Separations from their newborn baby.

● Experiences of rape or sexual abuse as a child or young woman.

When these memories come up, you may feel: 'Oh no, why can't I put the past behind me?' You can, when you have finished it off. Unfinished business presents an opportunity to take action and get it right.

One purpose of your feelings is to rouse you so that you do not let bad things happen again. You realise that this time you want to:

● Work out with your partner the type of support you want.

● Be more active in finding a really compatible doctor and a better hospital or homebirth midwife.

● Know more about your body, rights and personal preferences.

● You may just need to cry out your feelings or storm out your anger in physical ways, knowing this is justified, healthy and long overdue. The main thing is to be active and outspoken about every feeling and fear, until they are eliminated or at least out in the open where you can deal with them.

Then you are free to concentrate on all the positive and beautiful experiences in your pregnancy and birth.

Delight in music

Enjoyment of music is a lifelong blessing. Having rhythm really adds to your life in many ways — being able to dance, sing, learn an instrument all have their roots in early life. Whenever you can, have music in your baby's life.

1. Have favourite music to rest to during pregnancy and use this to soothe your newborn baby.

2. Dance to a favourite song when you are pregnant, so your baby feels the rhythmic movement as they hear the beat through the walls of your belly.

3. When the baby is born, dance with them in your arms, swing them around to music, move their arms and legs, and watch how they bob and sway and move their limbs. This will show you which is their Top 10!

4. Sing to babies, as you hold them close. They love to feel your chest vibrate, as well as hear you sing.

5. When they are able to hold toys, give them toy castanets, rattles, xylophones and drums. A shaker made from dry pasta or rice in a lidded plastic jar is just as good. Play along with them to a simple song on tape.

ANGER

This is another emotion familiar to most pregnant women. The first three months, when morning sickness is common, provide some reasons to feel annoyed.

You are surrounded by people saying: 'How wonderful, congratulations, you must be so excited' and all you can feel is seasick.

There's another aspect, too — something outside of your control is taking over. I call it the 'move over, there's two of us in this body' phase. The plus side is a delightful feeling of company — a little presence that is now always with you wherever you go. Even the morning sickness is a

It's the simple things like healthy eating and gentle exercise that yield the greatest benefits for you and the baby. There are excellent classes available in many areas to help both parents with nutrition advice, exercise, and information on labour and delivery, medical choices and even care of your newborn.

reminder that *this is really happening*. But what a reminder! You may be experiencing some of the following:

● Pressure on your bladder, which turns shopping trips into toilet tours.
● Sore breasts.
● Bowel changes and digestion difficulties.
● A general and sharp increase in sensitivity, especially in your sense of smell. For example, the smell of cooking, fish or strong perfumes can all send you dashing out for fresh air. Exhaust fumes, petrol at the service station and cigarette smoke can make you feel sick.

Many women also report greater sensitivity to outside influences, such as feeling more affected by TV programmes and more distressed by news items, especially about children. We are also open to other people's advice and affected by 'horror' stories which people seem to gratuitously want to share.

If you find yourself getting angry frequently, good for you. Your anger is alerting you to the need for changes; go ahead and make them. As with the fears, let people know what you want. You are pregnant — enjoy the power!

Stay around positive people and perhaps give the TV news a miss for the duration of your pregnancy. It doesn't reflect the real world anyway — just the collected disasters. You and the new life inside you are the real world. Learn to laugh. A funny video to watch (if you can handle the swearing) is *Robin Williams Live at Carnegie Hall*, where he describes his wife's pregnancy, including the mood changes — how he would have to come into the house with his hands over his head, kicking the gourmet ice-cream tub along the floor in front of him.

SEX

Many women feel healthy, sexy and full of energy. And sometimes during pregnancy a woman's libido drops through the floor. It's hard to feel sexy or romantic when you seem to have been seasick since the beginning of time. This can be difficult for your partner, so it's important to explain your feelings to each other and to be compassionate. Many couples find ways to give pleasure and reassurance other than their usual patterns of intercourse. Sexual interest varies from woman to woman and within the same woman at different stages of pregnancy. Enjoy the changes and variety.

SANDY, 32 'I just never felt like it. I didn't like my own body or how it felt, and Rob's attentions made me feel worse. One evening, though, he was less pushy, but didn't go off in a huff either. He just gave me a very slow, gentle, strong back massage and I started to feel glad I had a body, and stopped feeling like a sack of potatoes. I felt relieved and cared for, and was surprised at the extra energy and interest that were released in me to also care for him.'

SELF-ACCEPTANCE

The overall guideline is that, in pregnancy, you are *making space* — not just in your body, but in your mind, as well. And the way to make space is to clear out the junk. So express yourself; talk and get physical. Go into a bedroom and make a lot of noise. Beat up a mattress with a pillow, if you want to.

Miranda 'My first pregnancy had been quite easy so, when the second turned into a real hassle, with all kinds of sickness and pain, I felt really bad, resentful and generally negative. My husband had been very empathic and understanding, but that just confirmed me in being miserable. So he said one day: ''Well, there are some pregnancies that are very difficult. The question is, is it worth it, for what you get out of it?'' And I thought: ''Yep, that's fair enough'' and I got on with it.'

It's all right to feel bad, and let go. This will make room for relaxation, excitement and quiet joy to creep into the spaces you have made.

Whenever you are depressed or feeling stuck, the key to helping your mind is to move your body. Get up, get dressed, go out and get some exercise — even a short walk down the street and back — and notice how much better you feel. Try dancing, swimming or yoga. Remember the *goal* — this is a temporary state; you won't be pregnant for the rest of your life. The effort is worth it. One day soon you will have a little, soft-skinned, tender baby in your arms. Imagine this often — both of you healthy, relaxed, loving, happy, enlivened and content.

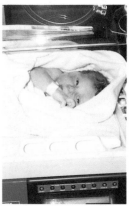

Parenthood 'Grows you up'

It's astonishing how early in pregnancy a baby starts to have an impact on your lives. There are now three people's needs to consider in every step you take. All the 'little' (!) considerations, like nausea, disappearing sex drive, and watching what you eat and drink, will wake you up to the fact that you are now a parent, even if the child is still a built-in model.

We've known of teenage mothers-to-be who have grown up overnight as a result of the experience. They suddenly become sensible, start taking care of themselves and sort out their relationships one way or the other. You see, being responsible, like being strong, isn't genetic and it doesn't come in easy stages. You just decide and you do it. In short, you are a parent from the moment of conception. This brings with it responsibilities; you will need to care for your baby, yourself and your partnership.

1. Care of your baby includes eating really well, avoiding drugs, alcohol, medication, fumes, chemicals, sprays and paints, photocopiers and UV lights, and, if possible, staying out of highly stressed work or other situations.

2. Care of yourself includes being kind to yourself and listening to what your body wants (it will tell you often).

For example:

● If you are feeling tired, relax. Take some time out for yourself.

● If you are feeling hemmed in or depressed, exercise, walk, go out and visit a friend.

● If you are feeling scared, angry or sad, talk it over, express it in some way.

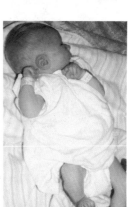

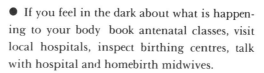

● If you feel in the dark about what is happening to your body book antenatal classes, visit local hospitals, inspect birthing centres, talk with hospital and homebirth midwives.

3. Care of your partnership means involving your partner actively and warmly in the pregnancy. He may not be sure he has a role or he might see it as a responsibility, but not something he can enjoy. Give lots of positive strokes. Do as much together as you can. Let him know you need his help. Confide in him first, rather than other people (but *do* keep up friendships and support of family, as well). Visit doctors together. Go to classes together, if you like. Do nice things for each other out of the blue. Enjoy some evenings out and treat these as special — partly because these occasions are an endangered species now.

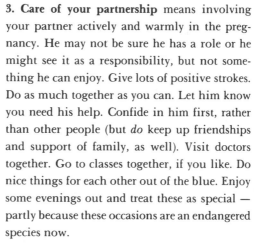

A NOTE FOR FATHERS-TO-BE

You can do a huge amount of good. Encourage your partner who is, after all, doing the heavy work on this one. Be supportive. Cook some meals — now and after the birth. Encourage your partner to walk with you when she feels sluggish or 'stuck'. Buy loads of really nourishing groceries and stock the kitchen as a surprise.

BIRTH EXPERIENCE

What will your birth be like? Unique. Dianne Mallet was willing to share *her* story:

For my husband Ian and myself, the birth of our daughter Amy was perhaps the most dramatic and impressionable event of our lives, although, medically speaking, it was routine and unremarkable. So much goes into making up the event covered by the words 'birth experience' that it is difficult to know where to begin and end. It is like sorting through old photographs, trying to decide which images are both significant and relevant.

I should begin by saying I am a trained nurse and midwife, since that coloured so much of the experience for me. I had delivered dozens of babies, but all my working hours were put in prior to giving birth myself. How differently I see everything now, having lived through the labour and delivery of my own child! As a nurse, I tried to empathise with my patients, but there is no way of appreciating the pain of labour or the joy which makes it all worthwhile until one has been through it. When I think of the advice I gave women in labour — 'remember your exercises', 'breathe deeply and the pain will ease', 'just relax' — I realise that, although the words were sincerely meant and seemed appropriate at the time, they appear mere platitudes in retrospect.

Ian and I were thrilled by our pregnancy. Though I was familiar with the information handed out in prenatal and pre-parenthood classes, we were happy to receive instruction at our local hospital in order to get into the spirit of the coming event and feel fully prepared for it as a couple. So much depends on attitude and I was determined to have a casebook pregnancy and labour, not to mention baby.

I am an organised person and used to

Navel gazing

This term must have come about from watching pregnant mums! One of the real delights of pregnancy, especially from about the fourth month, is the simple activity of taking a short time for yourself and sitting quietly with your hands resting on your belly, feeling your baby moving. Sometimes you can feel the gentle movements of tiny hands as they flutter about. Inside there, your baby is doing their own yoga or aerobic exercises. They already know that it feels good to stretch and exercise. Sometimes you will feel a much bigger movement — a strong, sharp shove — obviously a kick.

One mother we know had taken to resting her lunch plate on her belly (at seven months pregnant, she was very large). One day, her baby kicked it clear off, scattering sandwiches over her lap and on to the floor.

Some babies are downright squirmy and it's like carrying a puppy in your cardigan. Then they will turn over and stretch, like a cat getting comfortable for a nap, before sleeping quietly for a time. A good place to see these movements is in the bath, where the baby will twitch and move and change the shape of your belly quite markedly, especially in the last few months. Try to work out where the baby's head is and which way the body is pointing.

Partners and children enjoy feeling or seeing the baby. A mother told us, 'My two children reacted quite differently. One would say: "He's going to be a karate kicker!" The other would get very parental and say firmly: "Now settle down baby and behave yourself!"'

---

wonder how women could be unsure of their dates, but my doctor, the ultrasound and I came up with three different due dates, none of which proved very accurate in the event. A visit to my doctor in early May assured me I would not be going into labour for several weeks, as the baby's head had not dropped. Ian and I decided on a weekend at the coast, several hours' drive from home. After a day of walking miles along the beach, we went out to dinner, had a good night's sleep and, at 10 o'clock the following morning, my membranes ruptured.

I had explained this event to many women but, when it happened to me, I was incredulous. I had assumed I would go into gentle labour, spend several hours resting at home, then go to hospital only when I was about to go into second stage. Now I needed to be

Enjoy the anticipation together. This is a strengthening and preparatory time. You are now partners and parents. Help each other through the pregnancy and birth, and continue to do so when you have that baby in your arms.

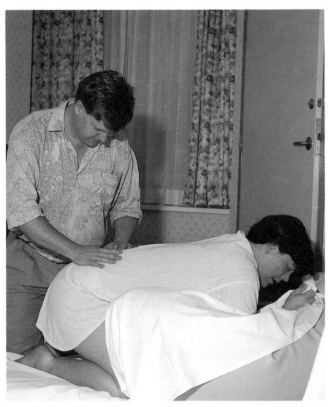

In these beautiful labour photos, the couple pictured is able to share the process of birth. They show the help a partner (or a midwife) can give with massage, breathing techniques and support. If you are not at home, try to get that 'at home' feeling by bringing comfortable slippers, a special photo, shawl, favourite music etc. or by having trusted support people available and involved.

admitted to hospital as soon as possible. Since the baby's head was not engaged, there was a possibility of the cord prolapsing and encircling the neck. I felt surprised, disappointed and upset. I also felt debilitated by the water flowing from me uncontrollably.

Contractions began soon after the membranes ruptured and we bundled into the car to begin the three-hour drive to hospital. I timed my contractions, while Ian cursed the wagons slowing our journey. We thought of the hospitals en route, in case I did the unlikely with our first and gave birth rapidly. I kept wondering if there could be another explanation for the flow of amber liquid, if we would feel foolish for cutting short an enjoyable weekend for a false alarm, but I knew in my mind this must be it. Even when one feels prepared for an event and happily anticipates it, the reality can come as a shock.

I was admitted to the labour ward by a sister who said 'poor thing' when I told her my membranes had ruptured — sympathy in advance for the long wait I would probably have in hospital. Contractions had all but ceased by this time and I felt that my doctor might do an induction in a couple of days'

time, if no progress was made. I was not keen for this type of intervention and my doctor had assured me he would not implement any treatment I was not happy with. But, at the same time, I was not prepared to put the baby at risk just for the sake of going into labour naturally. I ate a good dinner, not anticipating giving birth in the near future, and at 10 pm I settled down for the night. A bed was made up beside me for Ian, as I hated the idea of him leaving me.

Almost immediately, I began in good labour. Contractions quickly became strong and regular. Sister took my observations, remarking that the contractions were moderate to strong. I was intensely relieved, as I had little idea of my own pain threshold and felt that, if these contractions were mild only, I would be needing some strong pain relief before my labour was over.

At 11 pm, I was moved into the labour room and given the mask. I asked for it to be kept at its lowest setting, as I felt the gas did little, but the diversion of breathing into the machine was effective in reducing the pain. The greatest diversion, though, was Ian, talking to me of things, people and places we loved. He

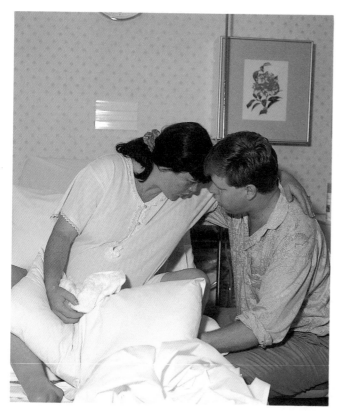
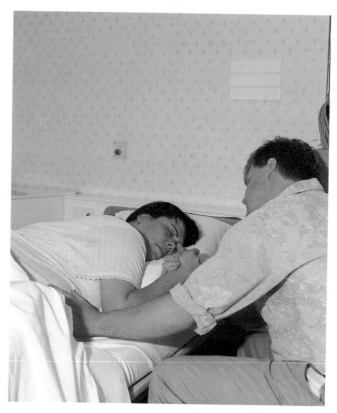

spoke again and again of the day before — walking along the beach together, the sea breeze, the smell of the ocean, the salt in the air and the stray dog which accompanied us for much of the time. This provided a very freeing image, one that saturated my consciousness and engaged my senses. With each contraction, I felt I would have to ask for pain relief, then, as it passed, I felt in control and happy to be working together towards our goal.

The young midwife assured me that the doctor would arrive in time to deliver the baby, despite it being almost 3 am. In turn, I assured her that I had every confidence in her ability to cope were he not to arrive in time. As a midwife, I knew the importance of the patient being as relaxed as possible and I wanted to assure her that I felt happy about her delivering my child. Ian continued to stand by my side, holding my hand and offering encouragement.

Just as I felt the overwhelming urge to push, the doctor arrived and, following a few more contractions, the baby's head was delivered. I knew from training that sometimes it's necessary to receive an episiotomy, and so I was not unhappy to receive a small incision. I was helped to sit up, so that I could see the baby's head — a slippery ball of blood and vernix — it was just beautiful. One more push and our baby was born. We had told the midwife earlier that we had only one name picked out — nothing for a boy — and so, as she was delivered, the midwife did not announce: 'It's a girl' but: 'It's Amy!' It was 3 am on a beautiful Mother's Day.

Ian and I had the baby girl we had hoped for, alive and well. She was three weeks ahead of schedule though, judging by her appearance and lung power, not at all premature. She was immediately checked over by the midwife, then handed to me to be put to the breast. Ian and I were in tears as we held our beautiful bundle. The placenta must have delivered easily, as I was not aware of it coming away. The doctor put a few stitches in my perineum and we were left alone with our child.

Ian climbed up on to the messy, narrow, labour-ward delivery table, lay beside me and held me as I cradled Amy in my arms. I could not imagine a happier, more intimate birth anywhere. We had been richly blessed. It was all over . . . and just beginning.

Be optimistic — expect that you will have a safe normal delivery. But be ready to accept that things might happen differently. Use your partner or friends to question, assert and look after your welfare — it's important to feel supported. Photographs are essential. Waste film. Have two cameras. Whatever kind of birth you have you will want to relive those never-to-be repeated first moments (and so will your child).

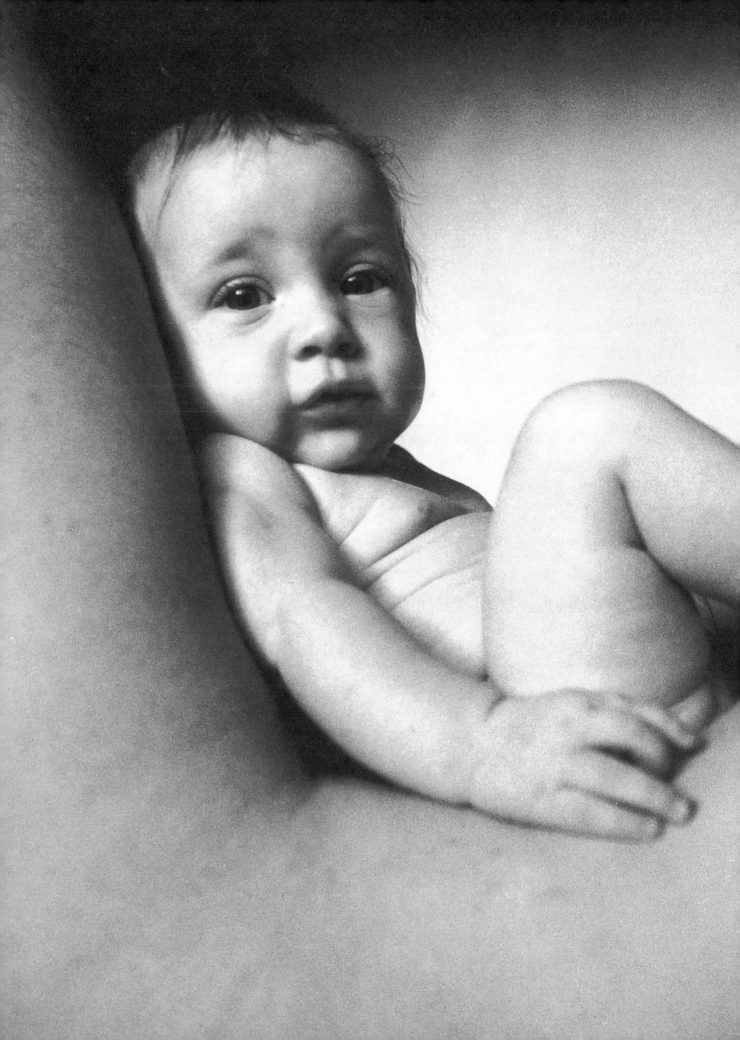

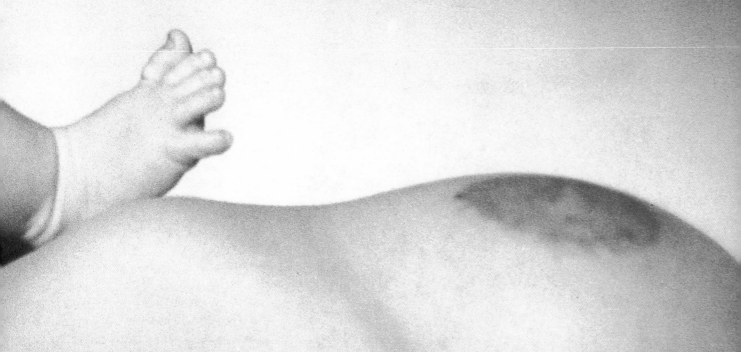

Babe in arms

Your growing commitment

Together and tuning in to each other. Making contact, exploring each other and realising 'we belong'. In privacy and using all of your senses —

- **the mother 'meets' her baby**
- **the father 'meets' his baby**
- **the two of you and baby 'meet' as a family.**

This chapter is about giving babies the love they need, while they are at their most dependent — from the moment of birth until they learn to crawl. It's a very important and beautiful time in your life, and a demanding one. There are three aspects to the care of your new baby:

1. Meeting and bonding with your baby as a separate person.

2. Your growing commitment, expressed through the practicalities of day-to-day care.

3. The fun of giving your baby extra learning and stimulation through play.

TOGETHER AT LAST — THE EARLY MAGIC

In the minutes immediately following the excitement of the birth, parents and babies find themselves wrapped in a cocoon of contentment and well-being. Most hospitals recognise the importance of letting the new family relax and feel in control. Parents should be able to state their wishes and have resources available to help, but otherwise be left alone with their baby.

This is a wonderful time to start *tuning in* — a process whereby child and parents can make contact, explore each other and realise '**you are mine, I am yours**'. What people do naturally at this time is exactly what's needed. Left alone, parents and baby might gaze into each other's eyes. They might gently explore, look at fingers, legs, shape of mouth, softness of hair, listen to each other's sounds, breathing and murmuring to each other. They smell, kiss, lick and taste each other. The mother's voice, and the father's too, will already be familiar to the infant, from the months of stereo exposure inside the womb.

Bonding — the sense of instantly falling in love with a new baby — is a real thing and it can feel like magic. But often bonding doesn't just 'happen' and new parents can feel disappointed. Medical intervention, or a mother being unconscious or too tired to really be aware at the time of birth, can interrupt the bonding process. We have to start actively building a bond, which will help us grow to **like** the baby and **find pleasure** in caring for them.

BONDING THROUGH THE SENSES

Sight   Encourage gazing time. Sit or lie comfortably together and simply look into each other's eyes. Research has found the best distance for babies to focus is about 15 cm from their face (which happens to be the distance to your face when the baby is feeding at the breast). Looking into your baby's eyes, as you soften and relax your gaze, you may notice waves of feelings passing through you. If your child is different from your expectations, or disabled, this can be an important time to swing between what you had idealised as the form of your baby and what they are really like. This helps the letting-go process — letting go of 'what might have been' and allows an appreciation of 'what is'.

Sound   Your baby knows your voice and will like to hear it. You will enjoy listening to the

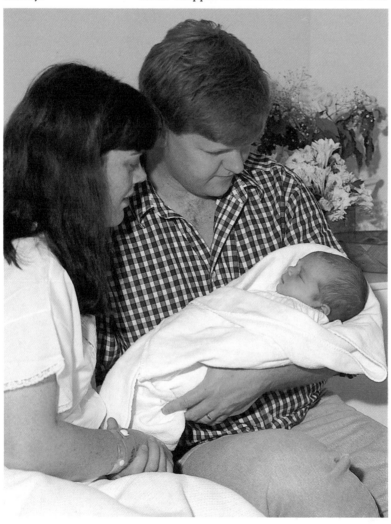

baby breathing and murmuring and, later, babbling and laughing. Babies seem to enjoy the sounds of peaceful music, your heart beating when they are cuddled against your chest or special heartbeat tapes, available from baby shops (though your own heart is better). Babies even like the lilting sounds of talking which, presumably, they don't understand. Many people sing and some even read short stories or poems to their baby.

Taste   We don't yet understand all that happens when babies and parents kiss and touch. Some subtle chemicals may be exchanged, letting them know that this is Mum or this is Dad, and triggering relaxation and trust. Most animals lick their newborns and babies we have known seem to love having the nape of their neck licked, and their fingers and hands gently sucked — making a game of putting their hands in and out of your mouth, and yours in and out of theirs. They will even suck on fathers' hairy arms.

Kissing must be the softest touch/taste combination that nature could devise. Parents love to kiss and gently move their lips across the baby's face and hands — even their feet. Babies' first kisses often consist of them opening their mouth wide and falling headlong on to your cheek, and licking up and down.

Smell   Babies have an acute capacity to discriminate between smells. They smell your unique combination of skin, hair, sweat and clothing, as well as your milk. They can detect which breast milk comes from their mother, preferring it to samples taken from other mothers. It is a pleasure for you, too, to smell their skin and hair. Later, it's valuable to be able to notice the smell of an ear that is infected and needs attention, changes in bowel movement or the acid smell of infected urine.

Touch   Although a baby can't understand the meaning of the words 'I love you', they can feel your loving touch, the comfort and security of being held, and the relaxation of being stroked. Specific touches you can enjoy together include massage and special baby yoga. Massage is soothing for both baby and mother. Time spent in a warm place, stroking the baby's body all over with oil or powder, will soothe a fretful baby, ease colic, strengthen muscles and promote digestion. You can time it to relax them before a feed or a sleep.

Baby massage

People have been massaging babies for at least 5000 years — probably forever, in fact. It has been proven medically that babies who are touched and stroked lovingly grow faster, recover from illness more quickly, sleep better, and have less constipation and digestive problems. They recover from distress more rapidly and are more settled.

Dr Frederic LeBoyer was one of the first to introduce baby massage to the West in his book, *Loving Hands* (Random House, USA, 1976). He asserts that 'we have to feed babies, fill them both inside and outside. We must speak to their skins, we must speak to their backs, which thirst and hunger and cry as much as their bellies. Being touched and caressed, being massaged is food for the infant. Food as necessary as minerals, vitamins and proteins.'

You don't have to be trained to be able to massage your baby, but it certainly helps to have read about the process and seen photographs. Here are some simple guidelines:

● Enjoy yourself — do it in a spirit of calmness and love.

● Start very gently, with light strokes for a short time.

● Keep baby warm and be seated, so you are comfortable, too — for example, sit on the floor with baby on a towel between your legs; lie baby on a rug on the floor and kneel above them to massage; or place baby on a towel on the table (but be careful and never leave them there).

● Take your cues from how the baby is reacting. If they are a little fretful, persevere and see if they settle down. If they really don't settle, try again another time, when they may be more receptive.

● Babies have very sensitive skin. Start by stroking their limbs and back with their clothes on, or when they are wrapped in a towel after their bath and while you are holding them close.

● Take two minutes for the first massage of a newborn infant, working up to a minimum of 10 minutes for a full massage with a baby of a few months of age or more.

● Talking, singing and smiling all add to the communication.

● Don't massage straight after a feed.

Quick and simple meals

Casseroles and quiches

These types of dishes are particularly useful when you don't want to be continually cooking complicated dishes, but need nourishment. They are not hard to make, have lots of protein and fresh vegetables, and can be re-heated or eaten over a couple of days. Where possible, make double quantities and freeze some for later.

Soups

Once every few days, make a large pot of soup. Wash, cut up and toss in all the vegetables you can find. Vegetarians use beans, vegetarian stock cubes, herbs and so on, or you can include meat or chicken stock, or lamb shanks. Include lots of parsley as a good source of iron.

For a quick soup, chop up some fresh celery pieces, or blend cooked vegetables or leftovers, and mix with a tin of commercial soup. What you don't eat straight away can go into the fridge and makes a good lunch or snack with toast later on.

Protein drinks

Make a large flask freshly each morning, then it's easy to have a glass to top up your energy and nutrition levels while feeding the baby. Combine any of the following ingredients: skimmed milk, milk, yoghurt, soya milk or fruit juice with egg, Ovaltine, Milo, honey, maple syrup, fresh or tinned peaches or apricots, banana, chopped nuts and/or brewer's yeast.

You, your partner, friends and relatives can prepare before the birth by filling your freezer with pre-cooked, nutritious meals for the early weeks and months. Pre-cooked and frozen meals make a great gift to new parents — after all, you can't eat flowers.

Movement: Inside your womb, your baby has been jiggled when you walk, turned as you roll over in bed, rocked as you move, pressed as you bend, floated in your waters and vigorously massaged by your contractions. Their early environment was rich in touch and movement.

Once they are outside your body, you naturally want to hold, stroke, snuggle, pat and rock your baby. Watch as someone holds a baby; they will almost always start to rock from side to side and sway their hips. We are very aware of babies' touch sensations — without really thinking about it, we want to put soft clothes against them, hold them in a warm bath for long periods and ensure they have fresh, clean nappies.

New parents are often accused of being too 'precious' about their newborn. Sometimes people can be quite rough and blase when handling newborn babies and it is new parents who remind us, with their focused concern for their child's well-being, that these babes are indeed precious and in need of empathic care.

Give your baby's father an equal opportunity for bonding. Many fathers will make sure of this for themselves, picking up their baby and doting — perhaps more than the mother expected or more than she likes — but the mother will soon see that this vital input from the father is in her own and the child's interests.

In a recent radio interview, United States paediatrician and author William Sears described how, after several of his own children had been born, he started to really get involved in the nurturing of the baby. He believes that fathers need to develop *comforting* skills which are uniquely male. He experimented with holding the baby close, with bare skin-to-skin contact. His baby also responded well to hearing Dad's breathing and heartbeat, when he put the baby's ear to his chest. The male voice vibrated through the tiny skull when he tucked it up under his neck and held his chin on the top of the baby's head.

Lots of fathers we know of have found the same things — that they can comfort and entertain, or quieten and put a baby to sleep, by providing some masculine care and attention.

TAKING CARE OF YOURSELF

New mothers can feel quite fragile for some time after the birth of their child, although many are pleasantly surprised by their rapid recovery. This is a time when you shouldn't have to move mountains or prove how spectacularly you can perform. A new mother is entitled to take time out from the day-to-day world to rest and enjoy her baby, and other people need to pamper, respect and help her to do this. If a mother can be physically and emotionally supported for the first few weeks, when demands are high and many adjustments are taking place, she will find she has more to give. It will then be easier for her to care for her baby and things will go well.

Helping hands

A friend of ours has this wonderful saying: 'Visitors are fair game.' Anyone who is lovingly involved enough to want to see the new baby and mother, or who simply has the temerity to visit at such a special time, can be pressed into service. They can be asked to wash up, vacuum, make a bed, chop vegetables, prepare cups of tea and snacks, turn on the washing machine and hang out clothes, hold the baby, talk to the mother, go to the shop or anything else which makes the mother's life easier.

The postman?
He also cooks us a mean risotto....

We know of a family who had twins and were in real trouble handling the workload. A friend circulated a list, asking other friends to put their names down to give cash, food or time. If you are shy, put up a big list in clear view of the front door. Entitle it: 'Ways you can help.' Your friends will feel pleased at being able to help out in a practical way.

During a recent high-stress time for our family, our friend Claudette began preparing and delivering an evening meal to our house once a week. She also picked up the empty crockery next day without even stopping to make conversation. It was a priceless contribution to our well-being — the casserole that saved the camel's back!

Importance of rest

Learn to get your rest in short breaks, when the baby sleeps. Put your feet up, have a drink and consciously let go of your muscles, close your eyes, breathe easily and deeply. Use the time when you are feeding the baby to relax, as well.

If you've had a restful kind of pregnancy, daytime naps will come easily. If you've been busy and rushed during pregnancy, it may take determination to retrain yourself. It's a trap to

Recharge your own battery

A group of mothers at a child-health clinic brainstormed a list of little things to do during the day to boost your energy and pick yourself up. They included:
- Have a cup of tea.
- Ring and chat to a friend.
- Go to Grandma's house with the children.
- Take the baby for a walk in the pram.
- Sit outside in the sun.
- Read a magazine.
- Eat chocolate.
- Play tennis while the baby is minded, or watch them in their pram.
- Watch a favourite soap.
- Take a shower.
- Bathe with the baby.
- Meditate.
- Brush your hair and make yourself look good.
- Go to a local shop and chat to the owners.
- Exercise.
- Invite a friend over with their baby, for adult company.
- Eat snacks or have a milk drink.
- Do craft work.

Occasionally, on really hard days, if you have been unwell or pressured, decide to have a time-out day. For many of us, it's not possible to have a reliable and loving helper to take the baby off our hands, so we have to do the best we can to have an easy day and allow our batteries to recharge. Don't do anything that isn't essential. Forget housework and extra jobs; your aim is to relax as deeply as possible and to enjoy your baby.

use the baby's sleep time to rush about tidying. A 'good' mother is a slob for these few months. Your well-being and that of your baby is more important than the housework! Your body knows what it wants and, when allowed to, will often fall asleep when the baby goes down and wake two hours later, when baby does, thinking: 'What happened?'

If you know or can learn meditation, this is very effective; 10 minutes of meditation can often be worth an hour or more of sleep.

Listening to music or relaxation tapes is one way for mothers to relax more deeply, realising that this is also a way to have a calmer, more settled baby. These tapes help you to relax very deeply, while being in contact with and taking care of the baby in your arms or in your womb. Restless babies can be calmed by the mother lying with them and listening quietly to beautiful music.

We have to start actively building a bond, which will help us to like children and find pleasure in caring for them.

GETTING TO KNOW YOUR BABY'S PERSONALITY

Each baby is unique and it's clear that they come into the world already equipped with different temperaments. As far back as 1959, it was suggested by researchers that about half of all infants are 'easy' (adaptable, happy, easy to care for) and a quarter are easy in routine situations, but have trouble with changes; the other quarter are straight-out difficult. They have come to be called 'high-need babies' — they can be loud, cranky, overly sensitive to change, with unsettled eating and sleeping habits, and their behaviour can drive you up the wall!

There might be a reason why a baby is unsettled — an allergy to cow's milk, say — so don't be too quick to label them as difficult. On the other hand, when all else has been tried, it can be a relief to know that — well, this is just one of those kids.

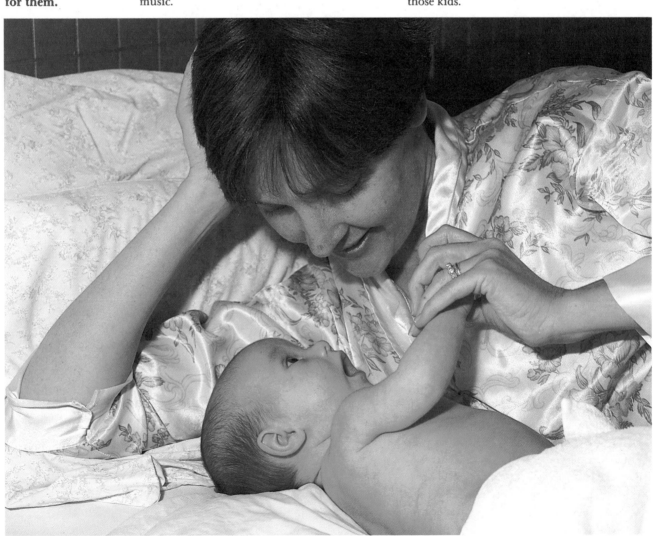

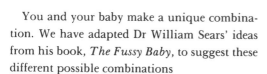

You and your baby make a unique combination. We have adapted Dr William Sears' ideas from his book, *The Fussy Baby*, to suggest these different possible combinations

Low-need baby (easy and settled) + **low-need mum** (relaxed and capable) = an easy time.

Low-need baby + **high-need mum** = gains confidence as baby proves easy to care for.

High-need baby + **low-need mum** = baby is a challenge but mother can handle it.

High-need baby + **high-need mum** = baby overwhelms mother's ability to cope.

(Adapted from *The Fussy Baby*, © William Sears MD 1990, published by Collins Dove; used with permission.)

While the above is very simplified, it is an easy way to see at a glance what you are up against and whether it is you or the baby, or both, who needs extra help. Being high need or low need is, of course, subject to change and that's the beauty of it. When a high-need baby tests your strength of character and capacity to endure, the only solution is to become stronger. This isn't done by gritting your teeth, but by calling in all available resources from yourself, your partner, family, friends and community-support systems.

Patrick, 27 'Our baby was diagnosed as having colic, which just gave it a name — no solution! The impression our doctor gave was that we just had to put up with it. We hated hearing our baby cry in so much pain, and thinking that there might be months of this distress. We found a paediatrician who gave us good, helpful, practical advice. We learned not to give up too easily.'

Kerry, 30, was depressed about how demanding her baby was, until her mother put it in perspective. 'My mother told me: "They're a big job, young babies. Of course you get tired. They're hard work but the time goes so fast. It's because they're intelligent that they are so alert and switched on all the time."'

Some of the useful community resources you could consider contacting include health visitors, doctor or paediatrician, breastfeeding counsellors, child-health clinics, pregnancy support services and social workers.

Reducing the risk of sudden infant death syndrome

Sudden infant death syndrome — cot death — affects a very small number of babies, but is so tragic that every parent these days is aware of it and keen to reduce the risks. While no single cause of cot death has been found, the following steps are known to reduce the risk and are, therefore, well worth following:

● *Always position babies to sleep on their backs or side*, not on their tummy. In some studies, this has been found to significantly reduce cot-death rates.

● *Breastfeed, if at all possible*. During the first few months especially, this is thought to give them antibodies to possible viruses which are believed to contribute to cot death. Some experts believe that breastfed babies are more SIDS resistant.

● *Quit smoking and don't let others smoke around your baby*. Being in a house with smokers is a known risk factor. (It also contributes to asthma in children, and babies born to mothers who smoke are smaller at birth and have higher rates of birth problems.) Preferably, both partners should stop smoking when you decide you want to become pregnant or when you find out that you are pregnant.

● *Don't overwarm babies* — either with clothing or by overheating their room, which needs to have fresh air circulating. A guide to what a baby should wear in bed is what you would wear, plus one more layer. For example, if you wear flannel pyjamas, babies wear their pyjamas with a woollen singlet underneath.

Research into contributing factors is going on all the time, so keep in touch by talking to your child-health sister or doctor, and watch the newspapers.

(Source: SIDS Research Foundation, risk-reduction campaign, *The Age*, July 1992.)

RECYCLING YOUR EMOTIONS

We've already mentioned the phenomenon of recycling — where old feelings from your past surface in the present. Often, a mother with a new baby starts to feel as if she is an infant herself — fragile, overwhelmed, frightened, unable to think clearly, emotionally distressed and vulnerable. This may be because she is re-experiencing the time of her own birth. If a new mother is treated with tenderness and nurturing, she will gradually find her strength and self-assurance returning.

Partners and other carers can help tremendously by gently encouraging her to think

Everything you do for your child's welfare is an act of love. As parents we suddenly appreciate all that was done for us as children. This stage of life tests and deepens your partnership and you appreciate each other in new ways.

through her options. They also have an important role in protecting her from too many intrusions and from the need to make a lot of decisions. They will be of great value, too, if they nurture with food, encouragement, massage, bed-making, house cleaning, the laundry, keeping her warm and carrying the baby for her. These things can be done with respect and thoughtfulness, not by taking over and ordering her off to bed.

In the rare instances where a woman has severe depression — where desperate thoughts occur to her often and family or friends fear for her safety or that of the baby — then professional help should be sought immediately.

Usually, it is the simple and practical little things which are of the most help to a new mother.

Stephanie, 40 'I distinctly remember the sheer pleasure and relief when a nurse brought me a hot chocolate drink and a biscuit at about 5 o'clock one morning, as I was sitting feeling lonely, sore and lost, with nothing to do but wait for the baby to wake up. I felt like someone had snuggled me up and made me feel cared for. I needed for myself what my baby needed from me.'

Janelle, 29 'I felt really sick and sore after the birth and I happened to tell one of the nurses that one shoulder was very stiff, from the way I had been lying. She got some oil and massaged it for me. I guess it was only a little thing, but it meant a lot to me. It helped me get to sleep and I really needed that.'

Julie, 36 'When my mother was having her babies, it was the accepted thing that the new mother could get outside help — a paid helper to clean and cook for about six weeks after the birth. This wasn't just for rich people — everyone did it — and there was no stigma attached. In other words, you weren't suspected of that dreaded disease, "not coping". It was just accepted as necessary.'

The point is, it takes time and learning to get it right with your baby. You show your love actively and show your commitment by experimenting to find what makes them happy. Soon you will be operating smoothly and with ever-greater confidence.

PRACTICAL LOVE IN ACTION

Bonding isn't just a feeling; it also includes a commitment:

● We have decided we will put ourselves on the line for our child.

● We will do the best we can and give our children what they need, even if it costs us time, energy and patience.

Most people will agree that the thing a baby needs most is love. That's true, and the love we feel has to be translated into action. A hundred times a day we show it with a touch of cheek-to-cheek, gentle handling, soothing caresses, smiles and words, easing our baby's distress with feeding and changing, and by *being there*. We put ourselves *on call* for our baby 24 hours a day. We don't let anyone or anything hurt them; we provide shelter, nourishment and stimulation, even when we would rather watch an exciting moment in a TV programme, read a book, stay asleep or just throw in the towel. That is love.

Sometimes it comes easily; at other times it comes down to a sigh and an effort to push on because the baby needs us. Love is not just the time spent gazing and smiling together like a soap commercial. Every act of assistance is an act of love.

Anne, 38 'The single most important thing I have learned about motherhood is to keep at it. I've had many different jobs and I've got several qualifications, but with all of these I had the option of chucking it in. But the job of mothering has been the hardest, because I can't resign or drop out — it's forced me to keep at it through the hard times, and I've learned more self-respect and self confidence from this than any other thing I've ever done.'

Rick, 23 'To be honest, I wasn't really into having kids. Jude got pregnant and I was still worried how it would be. When Elly was born, it bowled me over. I've stopped going out half as much; I just want to be home with Jude and the baby.'

FINDING HARMONY

From the very start, you and your baby will be working towards a harmony. It's like a dance where you gradually learn the steps together. You smile and they smile. They cry and you pick them up. You rock them and they gently fall

asleep. They become trusting and settled, and you become more confident.

Something you try may work one time and not another, so you move on and try something else. You gradually increase your 'repertoire'. For example, what can you do for crying babies? Here are some of the possibilities:

- feed them
- hold them
- change them
- stroke their back
- pat them
- talk soothingly to them
- rock them
- take them for a walk
- sing to them
- play music
- position them to relax their cramped stomach muscles (draped across your arm, face down)
- put them to bed
- put them in a bouncer
- give them a dummy
- push them in the pram
- make them warmer
- make them cooler
- burp them
- smile and talk to them
- let them sit up and watch the family
- ask for help from family or friends
- ring the support group CRY-SIS (0171 404 5011).

Which of these you try will depend on the situation and what you know of your child. Ask yourself: are they likely to be tired or have they just woken up and had a feed?; does their face look pained or is it a slowing-down, sleepy cry?

The best TV and radio shows for parents (and there have been several recently) feature practical advice, with parents and professionals sharing ideas to help you increase your repertoire of things to try with your babe. Because each child is different, no one thing works all the time. They teach us to be flexible. We learn to persist. A crying baby won't stop because you close the door or are tired, need a break or the phone is ringing, or you want desperately to go to the toilet. The baby's nature is to *insist*. Your job is to *persist*. Watch for their responses, learn what they like and provide it. Then pat yourself on the back.

It usually takes only a few weeks to really start to understand the baby's particular patterns. We help them:

- To feel comfortable, with a bath or massage, changes of nappies and clothes.
- To tire themselves out by letting them kick and exercise.
- To feel satisfied by feeding them.
- To feel secure and lulled into sleep, with cuddles, warmth and gentleness.

We try to time all of these so they are completed by the end of the day and the baby starts to learn to sleep longer at night, so we can sleep, too.

The art of breastfeeding

Comedian Robin Williams describes how, after six months of pregnancy, the most wondrous thing happens — the Breast Fairy comes. Both men and women are surprised, curious and delighted by the rounding and ripening of the mother-to-be's breasts and nipples as pregnancy proceeds. However, these changes are mild compared with the changes after the birth, when breasts seem to take on a life of their own.

A few days after your baby is born, you wake up to find two rock-hard mountains where your soft, comfy breasts used to be. Your milk has 'come in'. In the few days prior to this, your baby will have been practising sucking and getting small amounts of the incredibly nutritious, golden colostrum. Your baby has been building an appetite, and thank goodness for that, because you very quickly discover you need each other! Often, a new mother finds herself watching her sleeping

newborn and hoping madly that they will wake up soon and help relieve her of her abundant milk supply. This supply and demand link-up primes you to stay close and have frequent and regular contact through the breastfeeds.

Women have varying reactions to breastfeeding. Some find enormous pleasure in the whole process and are reluctant to wean their toddlers off the breast. Some are happy to nurse their baby, but pleased to stop. Others are unable to breastfeed because of difficulties, while others prefer to give the whole thing a miss and feed with a bottle of formula. Many factors affect whether you start and how long you continue. You will be trying for a balance between what your head and heart dictate.

The sensations accompanying breastfeeding are surprisingly strong at first. The 'letdown' reflex is triggered just after the baby has begun to

suck. There is a feeling of release in both breasts simultaneously; the nipples become erect and the breasts fill with milk from the storage ducts deeper in your chest and underarms. Sometimes, in the early days, your baby's suckling will stimulate cramping feelings in your uterus, called 'afterpains'. These are caused by the uterus contracting back to its pre-pregnancy size.

While your baby is busy on one side, the unoccupied breast may squirt milk, so that you need a pad or towel to catch the overflow. You will come to know the characteristic, slightly metallic smell of breastmilk, waking and sleeping.

You get used to being damp, changing shirts a lot and getting around padded up like a teenager with socks in her bra. After a while, you learn to take all this with good humour — what else can you do when you discover you've been out in public for a couple of hours with two wet patches on the front of your blouse!

All this has the positive effect of slowing you down and keeping you around home for a few weeks, while you recuperate from the birth and get into a rhythm with your baby and your own body. Things soon settle down and it becomes easier (and less messy) — a natural part of the tempo of your days and nights.

Nature equipped women with breasts and the amazing capacity to produce living nourishment for our babies. Breastfeeding not only passes food to the baby, but also immunity — something no formula is ever likely to contain. However, women are fortunate that, when breastfeeding is prevented by circumstance, substitute milk formulas are available.

We urge you to maximise your chances of breastfeeding with comfort and confidence. Breastfeeding is an art and many of us need a little help to get started. Seek information and support, such as ideas for adjustments to your feeding pattern and techniques, which will make the process pleasing and satisfying to both you and the baby.

The National Childbirth Trust has breastfeeding counsellors at a local level throughout the country. They can be contacted by phone or in person. They are experienced and caring mothers who will offer free advice on many aspects of looking after babies. Hospital nurses and child-health sisters can also help to make breastfeeding easy and successful.

Iris, 28 'My mother breastfed five babies and she was really helpful. She'd tell me what

Breastfeeding — the special connection. As well as building a closer relationship, we are ensuring optimum nutrition for the baby. Breast milk varies in its nature and quantity over time as the baby's needs change. Much help is available for nursing mothers through hospitals, health centres, and breastfeeding counsellors who specialise in helping mothers to breastfeed.

Sterilising feeding equipment[1]

If you are going to bottlefeed your infant, either from birth or after you wean them off the breast, it is important to make sure the equipment — teats, bottles, caps — is sterilised before each feed to prevent a build-up of harmful bacteria. From the age of about one year, when they are mobile and, therefore, picking up all sorts of germs from the floor, the garden and so on, you can simply wash the equipment in hot water.

Some parents opt to use chemical sterilants, steam sterilising in a unit, or microwave sterilising, again in a special unit. If you have six to eight bottles and teats, you will only need to sterilise them once or twice a day, instead of after each feed. Wide-necked bottles are easier to clean. Steps 1 to 5 apply to either sterilising method:

1. Rinse bottle and teat in cold water immediately after the feed. Leave to drain.

2. Before sterilising, using hot water, detergent and a brush kept specially for this purpose, wash bottles, jugs, spoons and any other equipment you use for mixing formula.

3. Rinse thoroughly.

4. Turn teats inside out and wash. Remember the insides get dirty too.

5. Rinse thoroughly.

6. For heat sterilisation, submerge equipment — except teats — in cold water, making sure spoons and so on are heat resistant. Remove any air bubbles before heating.

7. Bring water to boil and boil for 10 minutes, adding teats for the final two minutes. Dummies can also be added at this stage.

8. Wash your hands with soap.

9. Using clean plastic tongs kept for this purpose, remove equipment immediately.

10. Fill bottles with made-up formula straight away.

11. Cap teats.

12. Refrigerate bottles until needed.

Note Even if your baby has taken very little from a bottle, never save leftover formula for the next feed, as it will be contaminated with saliva.

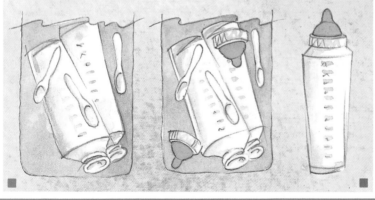

worked for her, like: ''Be careful with your breasts, keep them warm, try to relax because getting upset stops the milk supply, eat nuts and have a glass of stout occasionally.'' I don't know if all these were the right advice, but knowing that they worked for her made me feel I was on safe ground.'

Opting for the bottle

If you've chosen to bottle feed, have a talk with your midwife or health visitor about the type of formula to use and be aware of the content of the various brands. Also, ask about the different types of bottles, shape and material of teats, and how to sterilise the equipment. Mothers who bottle feed can make this as close as possible to the breastfeeding experience by holding their baby close, stroking them, making lots of eye contact. The close and beautiful experience of having the baby's skin against your own *bare* skin is also important, at least some of the time.

SHARING THE LOAD

From the beginning, you and your partner need to work out who does what. You can vary this to suit but, if the load is shared, it becomes possible to carry.

Sallyanne, mother of a handicapped little girl
'The way we got through those bad months, with a sick baby, cold weather and a terrible house, was to help each other continually. My husband would sleep in another room and get a good night's sleep. Baby Susan would wake up and have a feed perhaps six times a night. I could comfort her back to sleep by having her

in my arms. When she awoke fully about 6 am, I would be exhausted from light and broken sleep, and my husband would come in and get her and change her, play with her and give her breakfast while I slept. He'd also supervise the other kids getting fed and ready for the day. Just when he was ready to leave for work, he'd wake me and I'd take over again. By then the baby would be ready for a mid-morning nap, so I could clean up the house, have a shower and eat some breakfast in peace.'

Wendy, 35 'When my husband Rob gets home from work, there is a time he takes with our son Jackson that I really enjoy. He plays with Jackson and they have a bath together. I can get tea and still have a bit of time to myself. We eat, then Jackson goes off to sleep and Rob and I have a couple of hours to be together and unwind.'

We once asked husbands in a couples' communication group what they remember doing to help. Here are their suggestions:
● Bring home take-away food.
● Do the ironing — 'I'm an Iron Man!'.
● Clean up the house when mother and baby collapse into sleep.
● Pick up as you go along. Tidy as you walk and never add to mess in the kitchen or dining room.
● Do a late-night laundry shift.
● Organise family members as baby-sitters.
● Play with or take out older children.
● Guard against unwanted visitors and diplomatically fend off intrusions.
● Buy an answering machine, so you can choose who to speak to.
● And finally...'We were older parents, and had always said that a baby would just have to fit into our routines, that there was no need for disruption in our lives. We wouldn't let our lives revolve around a baby like these younger couples seemed to. Ha! The baby would just never sleep at night and had colic the whole time, and would scream with discomfort after a feed. The only thing that calmed him down was to walk with him over my shoulder for hours on end. When I stopped walking, he started screaming again. If I put him down, he woke up. I just want everyone to know that walking around the inner suburbs

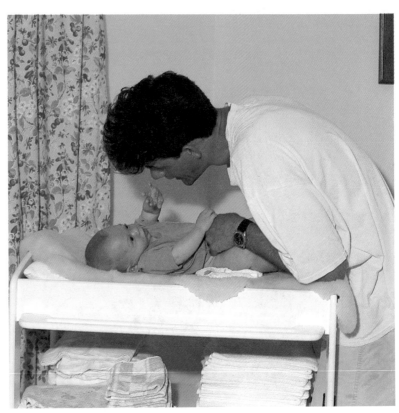

at 3 am with a bundle slung over my shoulder is what I want to be doing. This baby has *not* changed my life!' (Much laughter from the group.)

THE TIGRESS MOTHER

All mothers have inside them a 'being' or part of their character that they might not have known existed, yet which is essential for the job of mothering. In some mothers, it is instantly and obviously there the moment their child is born; in others, it needs some help to awaken. This part is ancient, powerful and fiercely protective of young life. It has many names in many places, but we call it The Tigress Mother. To help you contact this part of yourself, we suggest you experience what it might be like from the child's point of view — to be the recipient of Tigress protection.

Can you recall ever having been completely safe? Imagine what it would be like to rest in the security of a large and powerful caregiver, someone who is totally protective, and is dedicated to caring for and respecting you and your needs. Imagine a truly competent and deeply warm human being who, for a while, can take care of everything to do with the outside world. This

Couples are trying to find a balanced way to share the load. Who will work by staying at home with the baby and who will work and carry the major financial load? Many of us are coming up with creative solutions. And gradually we are seeing government and work-place policies seeking to provide for varying family needs.

Happy snaps

Take lots of photographs and be generous in sharing them with family and friends. It's nearly always worth ordering two sets of prints, as grandparents and other relatives love to have photos of children, especially if they live at a distance.

There are reasons other than generosity for giving photos away. A family we know had a housefire which destroyed all their photos and records. But, to their relief and delight, people were able to send back copies of photos they thought they would never see again.

person has your well-being and best interests at heart. Can you feel a sense of relaxation and relief at the pleasure of just *being*, without having to *do* anything?

In everyday life, we may have small glimpses of this degree of safety — with a competent and generous partner; from caring family members or wise and helpful friends. Some of us have little of this kind of experience and feel that in life we mostly have to battle on alone.

Secure, trusting and relaxed is what the child in the 'tigress's' care can feel. Now, at this point, think of a tigress, large and powerful, standing guard over her cubs, and imagine that *you* are this tigress mother. Does it surprise you how easily you can imagine the teeth, claws and muscles of a tigress? This is a fierce strength. As a mother, you will have to call on this strength — for endurance at times when incredible effort is required and for alertness many times during your children's growing years.

As you sit and think of your baby, you'll realise that you have made a commitment to this little person, to protect and provide for them, because they are completely helpless without you. This may come easily or it may be very tough, depending on you and your circumstances. Nonetheless, the bottom line is that a baby must be cared for — by you or by someone you have chosen for their competence and care. The tigress energy can keep you going until things improve.

Denise, now in her 40s 'When I was expecting my second son, I had a strong intuition that something was wrong with this baby. In my mind, I thought it might be some deformity, perhaps a club foot; I guess I was trying to focus on something simple and understandable. So I was very alert at the birth and totally keyed up to that moment when I would know if there was anything wrong. It was in the days when you lay on your back with your legs in stirrups and, when the baby came out, there was a peculiar hush in the room. I asked: "What is it? What's wrong?" The doctor looked over at me with a kindly expression and said: "It's a boy and he's got a cleft palate, but we'll take care of him for you" and they proceeded to bundle him up in a warm blanket. At this point, I did something which seems physically impossible looking back — I sat right up, with my legs still in the stirrups, and yelled: "Give me my baby — give him to me!" Which they did. I still see that obstetrician from time to time around town, and he has always treated me with respect and perhaps a touch of awe.'

Denise's son required a lot of assistance and went through many operations until he was 16 years old.

'After that last operation, I went to bed and stayed there, and cried for days and days and days. People were concerned about me, but I knew exactly what was happening — I was letting go of the 16 years of effort to get him back where he needed to be. I could now let myself be tired and vulnerable, and I could grieve but, up until then, the Tigress had sustained me.'

Awakening the Tigress inside you is one of the many beneficial side effects of becoming a mother. While not making you invincible, it provides energy, commitment and a heightened intuition which you might never have known you had. The Tigress may develop gradually or might suddenly be there in a crisis. The result is the same. You realise, quite simply, that you would protect this child with your life. It is the energy to do the very best you can.

BABIES ARE ALWAYS LEARNING

This is where it gets to be fun. There are much more interesting things you can do with babies than just feed, change, comfort and rest them. The babe in arms is a voracious learning machine and you can give them lots of input.

Babies are learning all the time. They strive to make sense of the world. Gradually, carefully, you watch them piecing things together: where do you go when you leave the room?; what is that sound coming from the TV?; what happens if I poke you in the eye? They are learning to use their arms, as they flap them around and bump their hands into their own faces, and stroke and prod the soft skin of your breast as they feed. Within a few weeks, they can bring their fist to their mouth, and find comfort in sucking and chomping on their own fingers. Soon they can bring two hands together and know that, if they aim in a certain direction, they can make the dangling toys on their pram bob and jingle.

After a month or two, they will begin to show daily advances in their communication skills. As you go to place your baby in the cot for a nap, they may stiffen their limbs and wail, letting you know that sleep isn't on the agenda just now. You'll notice them in the bath, splashing carefully so as not to wet their face, when only weeks before they were alarming themselves with their splashing and bursting into tears.

You'll find that you enjoy your child more if you *learn to notice little changes*. Experienced parents among your friends and relatives will often help by pointing out the baby's new skills. For instance:

● 'Look how he knows his mother's voice.'
● 'Look how she turned her head to watch you go by.'
● 'Did you hear that — that's her crabby cry; she doesn't want you to stop playing.'
● 'She's lifting her head right up now — she didn't do that last week.'
● 'Look, she doesn't recognise me with this sunhat on.'

Soaking in new experiences as they explore the world. Babies are ripe for learning. Having a responsive parent means the learning is even faster. The closer you pay attention, the more you will be delighted and rewarded by your babies' progress.

Teaching co-operation

Every day we carry out dozens of tasks with, on or around our babies. It's really helpful if they learn to co-operate, making our lives and theirs easier. For instance:

● Lying on their back, peacefully playing with toys on elastic over their cot.

● Having a bath quietly and happily.

● Having their nappy changed without squirming too much.

● Sitting in a car seat or pram and being content and interested in what's going on.

● Crawling, standing and, eventually, walking.

Sometimes babies acquire these skills easily, like a duck taking to water. Other times, we have to teach them to enjoy the experience.

The same guidelines apply to any new lessons you want them to learn.

Pick the right time. Choose times for learning, when the baby is bright, alert and relaxed. Good times may be after a nap or bath, or a short time after a feed when they are not too sleepy. Try again at another time, if this wasn't successful.

	BATHING	CAR SEATS	CRAWLING
1. START SLOWLY, with very small steps.	Stay very close as you undress them, then let them look at the water and feel it with their toes before lowering them slowly into the bath.	Take them on short journeys at first. Try having one parent seated alongside the child in the back of the car, so baby can see the adult's face. The adult can give them a finger to hold or a dummy to suck to distract them.	Let them have a little time on their tummy, on a rug or on the floor, with only a few clothes on, so they can enjoy the tactile sensations of the rug against their body.
2. MAKE IT ENJOYABLE. With words and actions, encourage the baby to start the new activity. Smile and give lavish praise for each little step.	Having a bath with your newborn baby is a chance for both of you to rest for a while. Babies love taking advantage of the availability of both naked breasts to have a feed. Soon they begin to see bathtime as a special treat and get excited when you run the water or go into the bathroom.	Stop frequently on long journeys and take your baby out of their car seat. Cuddle and feed them, then return them to their seat and continue your journey. Never hold a baby while travelling in the car, just for the sake of peace and quiet. In even a moderate collision, the force is enough to wrench the baby out of your arms and hurl them through the windscreen. All children should be strapped in whenever a car is moving.	If they don't enjoy being on their belly at first, leave them there briefly but entertain them with a musical toy or rattle.
3. PERSIST If at first you don't succeed, persist until you do! Whatever activity you are teaching children, don't give up just because they screamed the house down last time you tried it. Often, babies are feeling out of sorts, but will co-operate really well next time you try.	If you can only get them to sit happily in the bath for a minute or two before they start to cry, take them out and cuddle them in a dry towel. Then, when they are really calmed down, try them in the bath again. Their confidence will increase as they know that comfort is at hand. Always stay with babies when they are in the bath.	There isn't much option with this. Babies have to be in car seats (which are rather like straitjackets anyway), so most get used to it. But do your best to make it pleasant by association. If your baby is bottlefed, give a bottle when they are strapped in. They will soon associate the car seat with some measure of contentment and well-being.	If they seem distressed at being put down flat on their stomach, you could try sitting on the floor and draping them over your legs. Their knees and feet will be on the floor, so they can dig in their toes and practise pushing themselves to and fro. You can also put your hand behind their feet for them to press on.

LISTEN TO WHAT YOU SAY

As a parent with a baby in public, you will be witness to a very strange phenomenon. Human beings are compulsive communicators and, given a baby who is curious but wordless, they feel compelled to put extraordinary words into the infant's mouth. Have you heard these kinds of things said to babies:

● 'Isn't it a terrible world?'
● 'It's not fair, is it?'
● 'Who is this silly old lady making faces at me?'

These tell you a great deal about the adult making the statements!

It's hard to resist talking to babies and it's very good for them. It is natural to try to imagine what the baby is thinking and feeling. Parents will watch for tiny clues in the fleeting expressions on the baby's face, the tone of their babbling, pitch or rhythm of their cry and manner of their body. You literally put words into the baby's mouth, and this is how they learn to speak and understand the world. So it pays to be aware of what you are saying.

I almost cried one day when I watched a new mother in a health centre waiting room, proudly holding her tiny, exquisite baby daughter and saying: 'You're a rotten little tramp, aren't you? Yes, just a rotten little tramp!' — all this said in a warm and pleasant voice. This mother loved and was proud of her baby, but was unable to say it straight out. She would not really want her child to take on those messages.

Since the urge is so strong to talk to, and for, babies, why not say what we really want the baby

Beautiful baby

This is great for when you're feeling low, and maybe not enjoying your baby much. Perhaps they are teething, or have a cold and are wakeful with the snuffles. This is a good way to cheer you both up.

Dress up your baby in beautiful and special clothes, choosing the ones you most like to see them in. Apart from being warm and convenient, children's clothes are made to please the eye of mothers and other admirers. Gazing at them in their Sunday best may make you like them again.

Mothers often do this before visiting town, the child-health clinic, or relatives or friends. Babies attract lots of attention and friendliness, for themselves and their parents, wherever they go. Total strangers will comment: 'What a beautiful baby' and you will glow with pride as you head down the street. Grandparents and other relatives will be adoring fans, too, and all this can magnify your enthusiasm for parenting.

to think and feel? The power of positive suggestion is illustrated by one mother who wrote to us after reading Steve's book, *The Secret of Happy Children*.

Anna 20 'As the mother of a three-month-old baby, I was very distraught. The baby was hard to comfort, everyone seemed good at it except me and I was feeling so tired and depressed. Someone gave me your book and I read about "seeds in the mind" — what you say to your children — and I listened to what I was saying to little Angie at odd times during the day. I was horrified. I heard myself say: "You're a real little bitch, aren't you?" when she spat out some food. "You know I'm a hopeless mother, don't you?" "Nothing I do makes you happy, does it?" Stuff like that. I resolved there and then to change what came out of my mouth. I'll never know if she changed first or it was a change in me, but Angie became easier to handle almost from that day onwards. I think the change was in me, as well, and she was getting a nicer feeling from me that made the difference. I wasn't talking to her like she was an enemy.'

Sally, 31 'My baby didn't smile much. One of my friends would tell me how her son always smiled when he was put down to sleep or when he woke and was happy to see her. I was

so jealous! I just started saying to my daughter (of three months): "Who's a smiley girl, then" and: "You're a happy baby" over and over, while I smiled at her, and before long I had a happy child, too.'

Since we don't really know what a baby *is* thinking, we may as well have positive fantasies. When our son was two months old and continually crying and colicky, I said as a joke: 'He's really saying, "Thank you for putting up with me, I'll be eternally grateful to you." This cry-interpretation became a joke with my husband. Woken in the early hours, we would translate full-voiced bawling into: "I don't mean to upset you. Thanks for giving up your sleep to show me how important I am to you. I think you're a beautiful mother, Mum. I just want to check that you are still there."'

PLAYING WITH BABIES

For a long time while they are growing, babies don't give us much back. They can't actually say 'thanks' or 'good for you'. It takes a couple of months before they even smile. Babies can't give us a present or bring us a cup of tea. The best way to get reward from our babies is to have fun with them. They will be responsive and show enjoyment as soon as we put in some energy to smile and talk and touch them.

Sharon, 36 'I was one of the first mothers in our town to ever use a baby sling. I walked all over the shopping centre and to parks and cafes, as I hated being home indoors. As I walked, I would talk to the baby and point things out to her. People probably thought I was strange, but I didn't mind, because we had a good time. My daughter Sky is 14 now and has always been bright, inquisitive and sociable. I know this is because I taught her to be this way.'

There are two secrets of play with babies:
● keep it simple and gentle, and
● use lots of repetition.

Games start with very simple things done over and over. If the baby sneezes, you exclaim with a smile: 'You sneezed!' Your child, unsure how to feel, decides this is a happy thing and smiles back. Soon she will look to your face expectantly after every sneeze and smile in anticipation.

Disappearing games

These are games where things or people go out of sight, and then magically reappear. Disappearing games seem to be important for babies in learning that things or people go away but will come back.

Babies don't understand how time and space work. So, if they see you go out of the room, they may cry, thinking you are gone forever. For them, the present is all there is. Gradually, they figure out that you will come back and peek-a-boo games help them to make this connection.

Try hiding your eyes behind your hands and saying, 'Where's Mummy?' Then move your hands down and say, 'Boo! Here I am!' You can also do this when they are on their back, such as after a nappy change. Lift up their feet and legs to hide your face, lower them again and say, 'Boo!' Or drop a scarf over their head and let them pull if off. Also let them pull a scarf off your face and head, and laugh and smile as you emerge. A favourite toy can be concealed under a clean nappy, so that they look for it and find it underneath. Older brothers and sisters can play these games as their special contribution. They will often have more time and patience, and love to make the baby laugh by creating variations.

Some mothers play simple games, like taking their baby's fist and patting it against their little nose, and saying: 'Nose nose nose.' Then they pat the baby's cheek, saying: 'Cheek cheek cheek.' This certainly can bring out a new side of you. If you sound like a happy lunatic, you are probably getting it right. Our local plumber, Dave, was worried that his nine-month-old wouldn't learn to crawl, so he got down on the floor and gave him lessons until he got the idea. And it worked. We'd love to have it on video!

When you change your baby's clothes, take time to blow raspberries and hum against the skin of their tummy. Babies love it all — the closeness, the vibration and the chance to grab a handful of your hair. Tap their feet together, kiss the soles, sing a song. Enjoy yourself. Your child is a little banging, stroking, dropping, muttering, experimenting, reaching, grabbing, swallowing, tasting, sucking explorer. A genius in the making.

Babies will also play repetition games with you (whether you like it or not). They are right into cause and effect. 'If I drop this toy over the edge of the pram, it will disappear, but make a

Find out what makes your baby laugh. There are few things more delightful than a baby giggle. If you've ever fancied yourself as an entertainer, here you will find yourself an honest and responsive audience. If it's funny your baby will let you know!

Babies love what's good for them. Movement is very important in a body's development. Movements such as swinging, jiggling, turning, swirling, rolling, bouncing, swaying, help in the development of co-ordination, balance, and strength. Watch for the signs of their enjoyment and if they have had enough.

noise, and then I will call out and you will come and it will reappear, and then I can do it all again. Whoopee!' They squeal — you pick them up. They point to their mouth — you feed them. They reach up from their cot — you take them in your arms and hug them. They smile — people smile back.

This is the foundation of self-esteem: I can affect the world and the way it treats me.

You don't have to respond every time; they will learn that you don't always get what you want when you want it, but they have enough success to feel that life is pretty good and everything is under control.

Human beings learn by repeating things. Babies are self-programmed to learn, so they love repetition and familiarity, with just a bit of surprise thrown in. Watch as you start to play a game — your baby's whole body begins to dance and sway with your voice as you repeat a familiar rhyme or sequence.

Sandy, 19 'The first game that I made up, which really made my baby laugh, was this one. I would lie her on the floor on her back and sit in front of her. I'd hold my hands out in front of me and say: "Tickle tickle" and I'd slowly move them closer till I got to her chest, where I'd tickle her. Now she is laughing and

giggling even before I get there. So I sometimes stop all of a sudden and she looks for where the tickling has gone — and I bring the hands back and she is laughing again. You just make it up as you go along and bring in changes to surprise them.'

Fathers will often play with babies in much more vigorous and adventurous ways. Take notice of the child's reaction, not your own. Babies often love the way dads play with them.

A CHANGE OF IDENTITY

It takes a little while for some mothers and fathers to loosen up about play, especially to take time out from rushing to household chores, community involvements, work and so on. Perhaps you are used to doing 'productive' things, like going to meetings, writing letters, making sales and so on. Or perhaps you are the height of domestic efficiency, so that simply spending a languid afternoon with your baby, instead of ironing shirts or cooking wonderful meals, makes you feel guilty.

All we can say is, forget it. You are teaching one of the only human beings who will be wholly entrusted to you how to laugh, learn and love people. There is nothing more worthwhile that you will ever do.

How to fold a nappy[1]

Once, a nappy was a nappy, whatever the sex of the baby. Today, there are different disposable nappies for boys and girls. This is not purely a promotional gimmick on the part of manufacturers; anatomical differences mean that the concentration of urine is in different spots for boys and girls.

There are three basic methods of folding cloth nappies — the triangle (for newborn babies of both sexes), the kite and the rectangle. Generally, because they provide the most padding in front, kites and large triangles are recommended for boys, while the rectangle, with its thickest part at the back, is best for girls. Before fastening, always hold your fingers inside the nappy under the part that is to be pinned. This will protect your baby's tummy from being jabbed.

Triangle

1. Fold nappy in half diagonally, to make a triangle.

1a. For newborn babies, fold in half again, to make a smaller triangle.

2. Lie baby on nappy, so the base of the triangle is level with the waist.

3. If necessary, adjust size of nappy by folding down the top edge.

4. Bring up the point of the triangle between baby's legs.

5. Hold the point with one hand and fold one side over.

6. Grip both points firmly, while you bring the third point over on top.

7. Holding the three overlapping points firmly, pin them together, with the pin in a horizontal position to stop it poking into the baby's tummy.

Rectangle

1. Fold nappy in half to make a rectangle.

2. Fold the bottom third up for a boy or the top third down for a girl.

3. Lie baby on nappy, with thinnest part at waist level for a boy and thickest part for a girl.

4. Bring nappy up between baby's legs.

5. Fold sides under so they neatly overlap the section beneath.

6. Pin either side, with pins in a vertical position.

Kite

1. Place nappy on table in a diamond shape.

2. Fold down the top corner to make a straight edge.

3. Fold in the lefthand point.

4. Fold in the righthand point.

5. Fold up the point of the 'kite'. Adjust length of nappy to fit your baby.

6. Lie baby's waist on top (that is, longer) edge.

7. Bring nappy up between baby's legs.

8. Bring one side over to meet between-legs portion.

9. Place pin vertically over the hip.

10. Bring other side over to meet between-legs portion.

11. Place pin vertically over the hip.

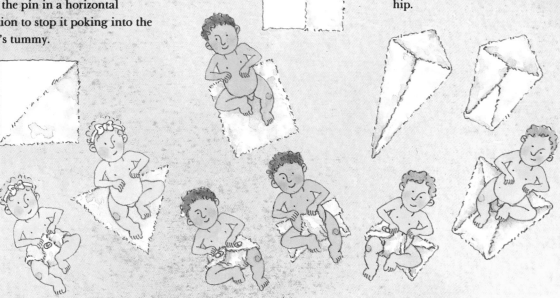

1. © Murdoch Books, 1994.

The mobile baby

Rhythms of life

By the time your child is crawling, you will be a much more experienced parent, having had months of practice. By now you will have discovered some distinctive patterns in the baby's day. There is often one longer sleep, hopefully at night time. There will be times when your baby seems particularly happy and active, and perhaps predictably cranky times, as well. Each baby's patterns are unique and sometimes, when you think you've understood what is needed next, it all changes and you have to think again. Don't despair — after a few months, you get to know how long your baby can stay awake before needing another nap, the average length of nap periods and how many they'll have in a day.

Some babies love to lie back and be waited upon (the pharoah approach): peel me a grape! While others are not completely happy until they can get their bodies to obey what their mind wants to do: "Just let me out of the starting blocks."

Julia's pattern

At seven months, little Julia:

● Wakes between 6.30 and 7 am.

● Is fed breakfast, dressed and plays until about 10 am.

● Sleeps for 30 to 45 minutes.

● Is up again about 11 am, changed, played with and fed lunch.

● Has an afternoon nap of 30 to 60 minutes at about 2 or 3 pm.

● May have a short nap around 6 pm.

● Has her evening meal, then a bath with her dad, between 6 and 7.30 pm.

● Has her evening breastfeed and goes off to bed at 8 o'clock.

During the night, she wakes once or twice for a quick breastfeed. Her parents keep the room dark, so she doesn't wake too fully. They are careful not to talk to her or change her nappy, in case she thinks it's play time. Because she sleeps in a cot at their bedside, they can easily lift her into bed and she doesn't get lonely, or cry or fuss. At 6.30, the day starts again and she won't be fooled into going back to sleep.

Julia's cousin Ben is eight months old and he has slept 10 hours every night since birth, with two long naps in the day, as well. Scientists are trying to isolate the gene which controls this wonderful quality!

Another child at the same health clinic as Ben had been waking for a feed every two hours, 24 hours a day for the first 10 months. Then, within the space of a week, he grew his fourth tooth, refused the breast and began sleeping through the night.

Do you get the message that all babies are different?

ARE YOU RECEIVING ME, OVER?

About this time, you might find you can distinguish between the crying sounds your baby makes, to know whether:

● They are hurt, from banging their head on something.

● They are angry that someone has taken a toy away from them.

● They are hungry.

You are forming a clearer picture of the baby's personality. They already show distinct tendencies towards being peaceful and placid, or alert and active, or friendly and co-operative. Some babies prefer people, some prefer toys; some are adaptable, while others are sensitive and easily upset. They are no longer a sponge-like newborn infant, soaking up the world. They are starting to be active and show their preferences. If you can figure out their needs, it helps you to plan for an

easy time. You may decide that the trip around Australia had better wait a year!

Bored? Play games!

There are times when a baby will become bored or impatient if expected to sit still — in a queue, on a bus, in the doctor's waiting room. Remember that babies love action. Together you can have fun almost anywhere. Tickles. Peek-a-boo. Hiding behind a couch or door and jumping out. Tugging their clothes. Making funny

faces or sounds. Using your hands like puppets. Letting them pull your hat off and looking dismayed. Holding their hand, pushing it on your nose and saying: 'Beep beep.' Lying them on the floor on their back and dropping a small, soft toy on to their tummy. Blowing raspberries on their tummy. Looking into a mirror together. Pointing out any animals. And whatever else you can think of.

The intrepid explorer

Here they go, off and about — looking, touching, grabbing, tasting, dropping, banging and exploring everything within reach. At the same time, the baby is getting to know their own body and how to make it work. Many hours are spent practising new skills — babies will rock on all fours, delight in arching their back, so only their hands and feet are on the ground, and look through their legs.

Later, they will insist on being helped to stand and will take both your hands as supports, making you walk all about as they totter along. Before long, they will pull themselves up to a

Tickle games

Hair Sweeping

Babies often like to feel your hair on their skin; try sweeping their tummy with it to bring giggles of pleasure.

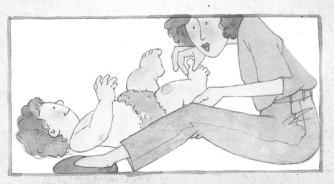

This Little Piggy

For generations, parents have played a toe game, while holding up their baby's foot for them to see, You recite the words, while taking each toe in turn and wiggling it around.

This little piggy went to market,
This little piggy stayed home,
This little piggy had roast beef,
This little piggy had none,
This little piggy went wee wee wee wee all the way home. (During the last line, run your fingers up their leg and under their armpit for an exciting burst of tickling!)

The Teddy Bear Game

The other great tickle game starts with you circling your finger in the palm of their hand.

Round and round the garden,
Like a teddy bear,
One step ('walking' two fingers up their arm),
Two steps (moving your fingers closer to their armpit),
Tickle you under there (running your fingers to their armpit or under their chin for a last big tickle).

A safe child is a supervised child. Take extra precautions in kitchens and bathrooms. The first simplest and cost-free step is to store or place dangerous items out of reach. Some items can be borrowed, other safety items can be made — eg. a stair gate. Safety should be a priority investment.

standing position, using the front of a couch, then clamber on to vacuum cleaners and low tables. They will enjoy slapping their hands on top of the cushions as they creep along the edge of chairs or couches. They love it when you encourage them. If they hear appreciative noises, they will stop and look back, smiling proudly.

SAFETY

Mobile babies can roll, crawl, topple, walk or drag themselves along. Children become mobile at different rates — it is not a race; they will do it in their own time. Sometimes it happens suddenly. One day you may leave them on the floor to kick their legs while you go for a fresh nappy and return to find them under the table two metres away, sucking a chair leg. It can be quite a jolt to realise your baby is *on the move.*

Having a mobile baby means everything has to change around the house. No longer can you leave a heater turned on in the corner of the room, as they can get over to it in a flash. What used to look like a clean floor, on close inspection renders up dead flies for sucking, coins for swallowing, pins and open staples for bare knees to catch on, loose plugs and wires for prying fingers, and newspapers for mushing to a pulp

with little gums. Your lounge room has become a sensory wonderland. You literally need a floor you could eat off, because that's what your baby will do.

Taking precautions

Some people recommend that you crawl around your house, looking from a baby's angle. A group of parents we asked suggested doing something about the following:

● Electric jug cords that hang down within reach. Move or change them.

● Routes taken by people with hot drinks or pans, who could trip over a lunging tot in their path. (Waiters in restaurants are not alert to babies — they count on customers being still as they juggle and deliver hot dishes and drinks.)

● Cleaning fluids, detergents, medicines, pesticides and other poisons or chemicals. Remove all these from low cupboards and put them somewhere higher, or away in boxes. In fact, sort through and decide if you can do without many household chemicals.

● Put gates or barriers across the top and bottom of stairs.

● Keep the high chair in an open area out of reach of benches.

● Keep fans and fan heaters out of reach.

● Always stay close when the baby is eating and cut food into small pieces to reduce risk of choking.

● Check for furniture — lamps, bookracks — that the baby might pull over themself.

● Install plastic safety plugs into unused power points.

● Inspect toys for small parts which could be swallowed, or sharp edges and moving parts that might trap little fingers.

● Toy boxes with heavy lids are a danger, as are piano lids.

● Be alert with the baby who is in the bath, as they will start to lunge and slip about more, and may try to turn on the taps. Never leave a baby in the bath, even for a moment. If the phone rings, ignore it or take the baby with you.

● Before you store them, tie plastic shopping bags in a knot to prevent baby from putting them over their head and suffocating.

● Throw away plastic ties or clips from bread bags. They are a choking hazard.

● Beanbags are also risky if the beans spill out, as they can be inhaled.

● Start good habits — don't let them play with matches, lighters, electric cords, power outlets, appliances or taps.

● Remove ashtrays and their contents from reach.

● Put screens around woodfires and heaters.

There are many other things that will apply in your particular environment — just look around and check.

It helps to remind yourself that you need to be alert and vigilant *now* whenever your little one is up and about. It soon becomes second nature to look ahead and check that the floor looks safe or the activity can't hurt them. You'll discover that other parents of mobile babies are good at this, as well. Start noticing little details. People who haven't had children around for a while don't tend to foresee the danger — for instance, leaving hot drinks on low tables.

Other children as carers

This is a time when other children are a great source of entertainment and amusement for the baby, but they cannot and should not be expected to be in charge of safety. An adult needs to be in charge of the baby's safety and should provide constant supervision when the baby is awake. If one adult needs to leave the room for a while to do the washing, cook a meal etc. another adult must take over the watching of the baby. We call this the '*hand over*'. One parent asks the other to watch the baby while they are busy. When they return, they say clearly: 'I'll take over again now.' Obviously, if both of you are around, both will be responsible for watching.

As the child grows, there will be more and more safe opportunities for unsupervised play. With practice, parents develop unexpected skills. The 'parent's ear' can hear:

● The quietness of mischief.

● The distinct sucking sound of a fly being savoured.

● The quick gulp that means 'too late' — it has gone down the hatch.

Parental intuition develops, whereby parents become inexplicably uncomfortable about their child being with certain people. Or they may feel a sudden urge to go and check the baby. For every 40 times you act on this intuition, with no apparent need, there will be that one occasion which makes it worthwhile.

How to teach babies to stay away from danger

Babies love to explore, but modern homes are dangerous places for a stone-age infant. With heaters, power points, hot liquids, high places to climb and objects to swallow, you must be ever-vigilant to prevent your child's innocent exploration from leading to permanent disfigurement or death. You can make the place safer, but you can't cocoon them, so you must teach them to stay safe.

If a child is heading for or playing with a dangerous object, *act first*. Pick the child up, or pull their hands away, and say in a serious voice: 'Come away' or: 'No!' or: 'Hot!' or: 'Hands off!' Take them away and give them something they *can* play with. This is deliberately worded, to tell the child what *to* do, as opposed to what *not* to do.

As children learn to understand speech, they will automatically think 'hands off' or 'stay away'. This is much more useful than what people often say: 'Don't touch it' or: 'You'll burn yourself' which is programming messages that you don't want.

Be firm and stay stern

Although it's entertaining to watch a baby determinedly trying to get back to the power point time and again, and you can't help but admire their spirit, resist the temptation to laugh. Tell your partner about it and have a laugh later. The baby could think: 'Oh goody, this is a game' and mischievously grin and head back in the same direction. It wouldn't be funny if they did hurt themselves, so take it seriously.

As the child grows, they can learn to feel proud of being safe, rather than always fearful of danger. This kind of training is also the earliest form of discipline, so it's worth doing well and creating a co-operative mood in your child. As children grow older, more explanations can be used and you can even allow small hurts to let them see the consequences of their actions. In short, for safety at this age you need to:

● Organise the physical environment.
● Keep the baby under constant supervision.
● Rescue them from danger.
● Start to teach them self-control.

Babies can't be naughty; they simply don't understand.

For them, the whole world is of interest. They grab a shiny 'toy' which happens to be a sharp knife; they don't know it's wrong. They have to be stopped, but smacking or shaking them will only inflict pain that they can't understand. And you might do real damage, which is what you wanted to prevent in the first place.

When you take a stand with your baby, you are not blaming — you are saying by your actions: 'This is not okay. This is a *limit* I won't let you cross.' These are the seeds of discipline. Here are some examples:

● Hold the baby's hands away from your glasses each time they try to pull them off, and say: 'No, hands off glasses.'
● A sharp-toothed bite on your nipple as you breastfeed leads to a loud, involuntary shout. Withdraw the breast. When the baby gets over their surprise, offer the breast again, carefully.
● Pull them away from the power point and say 'no' loudly, and persist until they get the message. Eventually, the word alone will bring them away, then they'll leave it altogether.

Communication techniques

Babies can communicate long before they learn to talk. When they cry, they are sending us a definite signal, designed to be unignorable. We feel driven to respond and the cry affects our biology — a hormone called oxytocin is released in preparation for breastfeeding. Crying just sounds like crying at first and some of us resort to stuffing cotton wool in our ears in an attempt to muffle the noise and soften the tension it creates inside us.

In traditional societies, babies rarely cried. Their needs were always taken care of immediately, they were continually 'in arms' and were remarkably placid. Hunter/gatherer tribes in all corners of the world still have this ability to keep babies happy. Prolonged crying, in nature, usually means the baby is in distress and a part of us gets very worked up at the sound. Perhaps this is the adrenalin we would need if we had to fight to protect our babies.

Whatever the reason, most parents at some time or other will have violent thoughts towards their baby, under the sheer stress of fatigue and feeling of failure after 'trying everything' to soothe a fretful infant. If you were hit as a child, you may be more prone to violent feelings under stress. If you are unwell or overtired, or if you have marriage or money worries, you are much more likely to feel distressed, so take extra care at these times.

All parents need a plan in case they find themselves desperate enough to feel they want to hit their child. These strategies work for us — you can add your own:

● Put your baby somewhere safe — usually in the cot.
● Leave the room and go somewhere quieter.
● Decide what you feel like doing to relieve your

Just like the rest of us, babies have their good days and bad. One minute they're up, the next minute they're down. "It's my party and I'll cry if I want to."

stress. If you feel like screaming but are too embarrassed, do it into a pillow. If you feel like hitting out, hit a bed or some soft furniture. Try and rip up a thick blanket or chomp it with your teeth. Run cold water over your face and hands; drink some of the water. Sit down and slow your breathing. Cry. Some parents keep a photo of their child looking really cute or happy and look at this to regain their sense of perspective.

● Get some human support, if you need it. Ring someone — a friend or a health visitor. This is important if you are having these feelings more than occasionally. You may be in a situation that is just too lonely and stressful, and need childcare or parenting help. Good parents go for help when they need support.

Baby talk

You will begin to recognise slightly different tones and rhythms in your baby's cries. For instance, a hungry cry might sound more forceful and urgent, compared with the weaker, lower-pitched, broken or repetitive cries of the tired baby before they fall asleep. Don't be concerned if it all sounds the same to you; you will eventually learn the difference between a cry of pain and a complaint which sounds grizzly but not distressed.

If you were to try taking a toy away from a mobile baby, you can imagine the reaction. They will cry like a car with a battery problem. It ticks over slowly — 'aaah aaah aaah'. The lip drops. Then it roars into action — 'WAAAAAHHHH WAAAAAHHHHH'.

Learning language

As babies learn to eat solid food, their tongues and mouths become better at producing interesting sounds. It's about this time that they start to babble. They also gurgle, blow raspberries and say simple words like 'mum-mum' and 'dad-dad'. Learning to speak is like learning a song — you get the tune first, then you learn the words.

Even in the womb, the baby is surrounded by the lilting flow of language. As soon as you like, talk and read stories to your child. Tiny babies will watch your face and the movement of the pages; they will start to see the pictures and enjoy hearing you making exaggerated sound effects. Small-sized books with thick pages, bright pictures and short sentences are great, as are board, cotton and plastic bath books. They can take rough treatment, like sucking and spilt cereal.

Each time children get you to understand them, they feel powerful and confident. Watch a grandparent with a littlie who is making noises at them and hear the grandparent pretending to converse. 'Gaaaruhgggh'...'Is that right?' 'Dagooooooo'..'Oh, I see!' The child will continue earnestly with the 'conversation' — a flow of bubbling sounds in response to the rewarding feedback.

Sign language

Babies can talk with their bodies. When you hold them, if they squirm and arch their back, making their legs slide down, it's likely they want to be put *down*. If they crawl over and grab your leg, look up at you and cry, they want to be picked *up*.

"I'll have some more of that, that and that."
"Take it away I hate it."
Long before they can talk children can communicate their likes and dislikes.

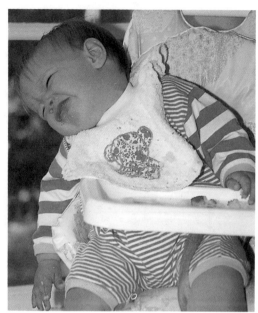

If they are crying and you hand them a biscuit, and they sling it across the room, that probably wasn't what they wanted. When you pick them up, and they start to bang on your chest, pull your clothes and bury their head into you, maybe it's time for a breastfeed.

There is no mistaking the 'baby smooch', where they gently lean a smooth forehead into your cheek or give you a 'kiss' with an open mouth and wet pulsating tongue on your face. But some of the signs a baby makes are more subtle, using small movements of fingers, hands and feet.

When her big brother crawls behind the couch, seven-month-old Jenny's feet start to jump up and down. She's excited. She knows it's hide-and-seek time. If Jenny is hungry and spots the bottle being carried towards her, she slaps a hand up and down on her side. She's ready to hoe in. You also know Jenny is hungry when she sticks a finger in the side of her mouth. This means — put it here. She chews her fist, as well.

If you see the baby staring at a toy, watch to see if their hand is opening and closing. If so, try placing the toy in the hand, then watch the response. They will soon let you know they are pleased you understood, by smiling and doing it again.

As babies get to know certain routines, like bathing, they begin to anticipate them. For example, when they see the bath running, they will pull at their clothes, knowing they will be coming off.

Each baby will have their own special signs which you, as the parent, will notice first, because you are most attuned to the fine details of their sounds and actions. Your responses will make the child confident in their first steps to reach out and communicate.

LANGUAGE SKILLS

Some children are chatterboxes, others are quiet. Appreciate their attempts to make conversation. Here are some of the words an 18-month-old called Hamish can say:

up	ta
tea	duck
bup (blanket)	bot (bottle)
bik (biscuit)	car
Didi (Lindy)	Dad
no (nose)	eye
at (hat)	shree (three)
Amik (Hamish)	bow (boat)
Amy (Emma)	fruw (fruit)
shiut (shut)	poo
pis (penis)	butn (belly button)
gen (again, as in 'do it again')	
more	yes
by	bart (bath)
cup	buttet (bucket)
Mama	ear
onj (orange)	Show (Sophie)
jiji (horse)	wee
no	eeeeeee (fly)

There are many more words Hamish can understand, but not yet wrap his lips around.

GROWING COMPETENCE

As their first birthday approaches, most babies are taking solid food and drinking from a bottle or cup. They are becoming more a part of normal family activities, instead of the family revolving around them. Even their diet will be less special and they can handle small amounts of what the family is eating.

As babies begin to eat solids, they will naturally reach for the spoon and 'help' to put the food in their mouth (or on hair or clothes). They will also grab and control their own cup or bottle, and pick up small pieces of soft food and feed themselves. As children learn to feed themselves, their confidence and contentment grow. It's a bonus for parents, too. These accomplishments continue, with sitting up, crawling, creeping and walking, and playing contentedly on their own (for up to 15 seconds!).

A single mother wrote to us, concerned about her six-month-old crying each time she left the room. Was he too clinging? We felt confident that this baby was doing well. He was noticing what his mother was doing and communicating assertively, and will be highly motivated to get on with his next job of learning to crawl along the floor to see where Mum has gone.

Trust through familiarity

After a while, routines will start to make sense to babies and they will anticipate what comes next. For example, at six months of age, Tamara hated her car seat. Strapping her in would bring howls of protest. Now, at one year, the mention of 'school', 'car' and 'brother', in any order, magically removes the fuss.

Having rituals and order in your daily life help babies know where they are and build up a sense of trust. Relationships are strengthening now. They love familiar faces and places.

The first birthday

As you look back on all that your baby has learned in a short 12 months, you will be amazed. You will also glow with pride as you realise that you, as their parents, have made the investment of care, sheer physical effort and loving attention to detail which has brought your baby this far. Whatever happens in the future, nothing will take this away and nothing will equal the importance of this first year.

Go and buy yourself a present. You deserve it.

Birthday letters

A woman once related a beautiful story to us about her father. She had experienced many problems with him, both when she was growing up and as an adult. Even after his death, she had unresolved feelings. Then she discovered a letter he had written to her when she was only one year old. It accompanied a teddy bear and now, at 40, she treasures the bear and the letter because she really didn't know until then that her father had loved her and felt so gently towards her.

Since hearing this story, we have written (and kept in a safe place) yearly birthday letters that describe to our children what is happening in their lives at the time of their birthday — their achievements, likes, dislikes and special events. Here's an example:

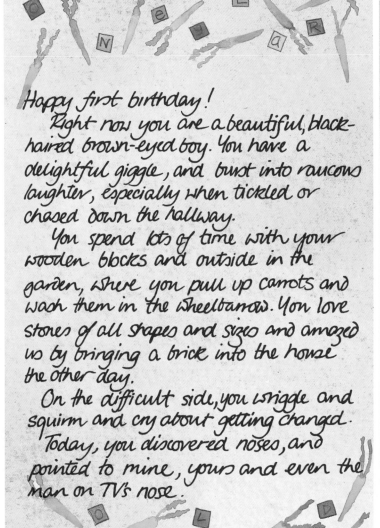

Happy first birthday!

Right now you are a beautiful, black-haired brown-eyed boy. You have a delightful giggle, and burst into raucous laughter, especially when tickled or chased down the hallway.

You spend lots of time with your wooden blocks and outside in the garden, where you pull up carrots and wash them in the wheelbarrow. You love stones of all shapes and sizes and amazed us by bringing a brick into the house the other day.

On the difficult side, you wriggle and squirm and cry about getting changed.

Today, you discovered noses, and pointed to mine, yours and even the man on TV's nose.

Toddlers 2-4

Toddlers are impressive

Children of this age are emerging as real little people — you can talk together and have a true sense of companionship. Toddlers are fast and keep you on your toes. They are creative, getting into everything they can and some things they can't. They look for trouble and, if they're lucky, the worst thing they'll meet is you. It's the age of full-on learning.

In this chapter, we'll look at the four most-asked questions for this age group:

1. How to handle discipline and get co-operation from these energetic and independent children.

2. How to teach toddlers to help themselves (and you) around the house.

3. How to look after yourself and your partnership during these robust years.

4. How to have fun with an age group that specialises in this quality.

"She took my sand!" Co-operative play takes a while to learn. It actually takes a lot of time and practice. They need us to show them what to do and encourage them when they get it right.

DISCIPLINE

Why toddlers look for trouble — and how to give it to them!

Imagine this. Little Donald is visiting your house with his mother. You serve cake with jam on it. Donald rubs the jam on to your couch. His mother tells him not to, so he drops the cake on the floor and treads it into the carpet. His mother shouts at him and he runs off. She says: 'Come back' and he doesn't. He hides under the bed and won't come out.

Everyone knows a Donald and no one is all that surprised — at this age, discipline is the big question in almost every parent's mind. Babies are hard work, teenagers can be a worry. But parents, grandparents, childcarers, teachers, even truck drivers know — toddlers are tough.

Why is this so? What is it that changes them from sweet infants into machines of destruction? The answer is simple — it's because they are now super mobile, super smart and entering a stage (known to most people as the terrible twos) where they actually *need* to experience lots of conflict in order to turn into emotionally healthy children in the long run. It's like Vitamin S (for struggle) and every child needs it to grow.

This is the paradox of parenting — that while our job with *infants* has been geared to keeping them happy, our job with *toddlers* is often quite the opposite. We need to let them be *uncomfortable*, briefly but definitely, many times a day. Not because we want to, and never with cruelty, but so that they can learn to handle life.

A toddler is entering a different phase of life and needs a different kind of love. Newborn babies are at the centre of their own universe. They want only what they need and it's our job to fill those needs. Babies' needs are simple — food, comfort, stimulation and loving touch. But toddlers are different. They want the world! They want you to open the ice-cream store just for them. They want to play in the traffic. They want to post sliced bread into the front of your VCR (to see if a loaf appears on the TV). Even the most indulgent parent soon realises that toddlers cannot be allowed to do what they want . . . at least, not all the time.

This calls for a different kind of capacity in parents. On top of all the soft and generous love you have been giving, you now have to add some 'tough' loving — to set some limits and boundaries, and allow natural frustrations for your child. It's through learning to live within these limits that they learn to be happy in the world.

Preparing for the real world

Step back from your parenting job for a moment and look at what you are really aiming for. Your job is clear. You have about 18 years in which to train a child for life. Your aim is to produce a person who can make it in the real world — be happy, take care of themselves, get along with others, stay out of jail and perhaps even make a contribution to society.

Think about some of the rules operating in the real world, which you and I have to deal with routinely:

- You can't always have what you want.
- Other people have feelings, too.
- Hitting people is not on.
- Some things take time.
- Your feelings don't change the world.
- Think first, act second.

These are lessons a child has to come to grips with, in thousands of practical situations, in the toddler years and beyond. They can best learn them from you — as you love them and teach them in a good-humoured, balanced way. The outside world will teach them, also, but not so caringly. If parents don't get discipline right, children, teachers and others will not be able to build on it.

Not everyone learns these things and there are plenty of adults who go through life having tantrums, hurting people, acting impulsively and so on. But they are not happy people and no one likes them.

Let's get specific. You're at the supermarket checkout. Three-year-old Johnny sees the sweets hanging close at hand. He wants them. At this age, seeing is wanting is getting because, until now, that has mostly been true. But you, as his parent, do not agree. This time, no sweets, for any number of good reasons — it's almost mealtime, that colour makes him hyperactive, you're broke or you just don't believe in giving kids what they ask for every time.

Feelings and faces

This is a very valuable activity, yet it needs no planning — just some time when you are together and the opportunity occurs. In it, you use facial expressions to teach your child about different feelings.

'This is a sad face. See, my mouth is drooping. My head is leaning forward. My eyes are looking down. I might sniff or cry. Can you do a sad face?'

'This is an angry face. My eyebrows are pushed together and down. I'm staring hard with my eyes. My teeth are tight. My lips are pushed together. Can you make an angry face?'

'Now I'm scared. I'm biting my bottom lip. My forehead is crinkled. My eyes look about quickly. My shoulders are hunched up. Can you make a scared face?'

'This is a happy face. My mouth is smiling. My skin is soft. I might even be laughing. Now you show me happy. Sad. Angry. Scared.'

'Now you guess which one I'm showing you.'

Benefits: This speeds up the process whereby children learn to read, in a person's face and behaviour, what that person might be feeling. It leads on to helping them to know the most useful ways to act around a person who is having strong feelings. It encourages children to be sensitive and helps them to be good with people. Finally, and perhaps most importantly, it helps them to understand and express *their* feelings.

**Tantrums —
learning you can't
always get what you
want. Up till now if
they cried we'd feed
them. If they cried
louder — we'd do it
twice as fast. Now
they are older we are
expecting to see
them develop some
self-control.
Learning to wait,
take "no" for an
answer, say what
they want and listen,
are some of the
important lessons.
No wonder it's tough
on us and them! We
want them to keep
their beautiful spirit
— and be able to rein
it in and direct their
energies.**

You say 'no', firmly. Johnny has never experienced this before and he doesn't wait long before responding. The 'wanting energy' in his body builds up rapidly and he is *off*. He is on the floor, screaming and hitting at your legs, the trolley, the whole bit. He is having his first public tantrum.

What do you *do*? It doesn't really matter — whatever is necessary. Smile sweetly at the check-out operator, pay your bill, pretend you are always this shade of purple and hope that he will stop eventually. Or grab him and take him screaming to the car, leaving your groceries behind. Or hold him firmly and tell him repeatedly: 'I'm waiting for you to stop and talk normally' until he does. All of these have been tried successfully by parents we've talked with. What matters, though, for future life is the *aftermath* — it's this that decides whether this is the first and last tantrum or the beginning of a life of embarrassment.

Think about what little Johnny has done. He has taken the discomfort he is feeling and shifted it to you. This isn't planned — it just works that way. You feel embarrassed, mean or unnerved by his reaction, and (he hopes) you may think: 'Well, one packet of sweets can't do any harm.'

For the prepared parent, this isn't a crisis — it's a *learning opportunity*. Johnny is learning how to handle a little disappointment — to take 'no' for an answer from time to time and to contain his feelings in consideration of others. These are some of life's *big lessons*.

So the way you help him is by not letting him get away with it. Give him back the discomfort he is trying to put on to you. When you ignore him or walk away, he realises nothing is going to happen in his favour. Don't ever give your child the sweets or other reward which was the whole point of the tantrum.

If you scruff him and drag him to the car, you are giving him back some of the discomfort you felt. Not yelling abuse, not hitting or being cruel or cold, but some tough talking. It's fine to sound as angry and loud as you feel at the time, but choose your words with care — you're not supposed to have a counter-tantrum. You could say something like: 'I was embarrassed and angry. I don't feel like being nice to you right now' or: 'I don't feel like I want to take you shopping any more. You need to think about what you did and fix that up with me.' Even at three years of age, the message will get through: 'Mum is not happy.' The aim is that Johnny's discomfort continues, until at the very least he: 1. says he is sorry and/or 2. tells you what he should have done differently. Make sure he knows what to do next time.

With children of two, the aim is more often for them to:
● Calm down.
● Take 'no' for an answer.
● Find something else to do.

This all takes repetition. You need to be capable of a little drama. A strong voice and a stern face are very useful. So is the grit to 'hang in' there until a child gets the message: 'Oh, boy! That just wasn't worth the trouble.' Once you and little Johnny understand each other, your relationship can go back to being friendly and fun. No leftovers; just a problem solved.

Most of us have trouble early on with discipline, because it is one of life's big ones. It calls on all kinds of qualities in us which, before parenthood, may never have been needed. Rate yourself on the following qualities (1 = not very good at it, 5 = brilliant).

You can be angry, but stay steady and safe at the same time.   1—2—3—4—5
You do not mind having someone (your child) hating you intensely for brief periods.
1—2—3—4—5
You are willing to hang in with something and not give in.   1—2—3—4—5
You are able to think well under pressure.
1—2—3—4—5

Helpful suggestions for parents:
- **learn to listen to your child's point of view**
- **develop a few clear and simple rules like "no hitting" etc.**
- **respond quickly to prevent a problem getting "wound up"**
- **plan ahead, avoid unnecessary stress**
- **helping a child through problems strengthens your relationship.**

You believe that *your* feelings and needs are important, too.   1—2—3—4—5

You can be a bit of an actor — tough on the outside, while staying basically loving on the inside.   1—2—3—4—5

These all come with practice. Your own childhood will influence how you react and you may have to perform some therapy on yourself. Perhaps your parents were hitters or withdrew their affection or used guilt and shame or were marshmallows who always gave in to you. If that's so, you will want to find a better way with your children. Welcome to the club.

How children try to give *us* the problem

Children are good at psyching us out. They quickly learn which strategy is most likely to succeed. Suppose we are prone to feeling guilty.

We smoked a cigarette when we were pregnant. We accidentally left our child on the bus when they were two months old. We gave them juice bottles and found out later that it can rot their teeth. Now we harbour deep feelings of guilt and remorse. This means that we are an easy mark for the *sulking child*. They pull a pout, drop a lip, blink back a tear and we buy them anything.

Other parents are fearful of conflict and so easy marks for *Tantrum Kid*. They have noticed our reaction to their original tantrum (the free one, that all kids have). They now have 'got it down' and watch closely for audience response as they bring in extra effects — the dribble on the floor, head banging, hyperventilation and bugged-out eyes.

Other parents are peace-and-quiet lovers, ripe for blasting by The *Whinger*. This child knows how to pitch their voice at just the right level for total irritation.

Or we are protective and proud of our understanding and empathic ways. A good match for little *Miss/Master Cute-and-Shy*. They are too 'scared' to do anything or try anything, so we do it all for them. A real hit with grandparents.

We're being a bit mean here. Kids are beautiful and creative, and they all do most of these things from time to time. It only becomes a problem if the behaviour gets out of hand, which is only if we let them get away with it too often. So what are the alternatives?

'Stand and think'

This is a discipline method which really works. The aim is to train children in how to behave. We don't want them to be wimps or bullies. We want them to get their needs met and get along with other people.

Somehow, at this age, children have to learn how to stop themselves — to wait their turn, not hit another child or give up on something they aren't going to get. We have to provide firmness on the outside, so that they can develop it on the inside. Old approaches tended to punish rather than train. Parents would usually follow a time-honoured sequence of deteriorating control:

1. Ask sweetly.
2. Ask firmly (but with a quavering voice).
3. Ask angrily.
4. Threaten to hit.
5. Hit.
6. Feel terrible.

Making a special play space

Kids like to have a spot of their own — a seat, room, desk, cubby or whatever. Sometimes deliberately creating a separate space can help a child to concentrate on an activity, and let them feel special and powerful. It doesn't have to be big, expensive or separately built.

Boxes

Collect boxes from supermarkets — they create fabulous castles, forts, shops, shelves, cars, targets for bowling or goals for throwing a ball into to increase ball skills. If you get one big box (from appliance shops), all the smaller ones can be stored in it.

Couch

Pull the couch out a little, creating a special cubby space between couch and wall. It's a good place to spy on Mum and the jumble of toys can stay there out of sight.

The 'nest'

This is wonderful for a child who wants to be part of the action all of the time. They may not want their daily sleep any more, and become tired and grumpy — not wanting to rest but at the same time not able to stay up. Look out for a big, open, low basket or cut down a large cardboard box, into which you can place pillows, sheepskins or soft blankets to make a 'nest'. This is the resting place, where a bottle of juice can be consumed at leisure, while watching Playschool or listening to taped music or a story. Little children love to snuggle in a nest; it becomes associated in their mind with 'quiet time'. If they talk or get up, nest time is over.

Knock to enter

Bedrooms matter a lot to children. At particular times, you may notice that your child wants a little more privacy. Perhaps they want to be treated as an individual or they just get a fright when people burst into their room. Experiment with knocking first and asking, 'Can I come in?' It's surprising how children feel more confident and respected by this simple courtesy.

The mother turtle game

This is a warm-hearted game, symbolic of healthy growing up, from a secure beginning. Like all games which involve getting down on the carpet or lawn with your child, it brings closeness and fun for everyone.

Help your child to roll into a small ball on the ground. They are now a turtle egg. The mother turtle (you) covers the child's body with hers and folds her arms around the front of the child's head, being careful not to 'break the egg'. She then tells a short story — that she is a big, strong and proud mother turtle, who has laid her special egg in the warm sand. With her hands flattened out, she pretends to scoop warm sand up and over the turtle egg to keep it safe and warm. She says: 'Nobody can touch my egg' and slaps the surrounding ground to protect the egg.

'But wait a minute,' she says, 'what is that? A little wriggle?' Then there are lots of wriggles coming from the egg. 'It must be ready to hatch. Yes!' Out comes a beautiful, shiny, new turtle who is off to play in the sand and swim in the sea. When sharks or big fish come, it swims straight back. It can go to sleep in the nest, then head off again.

Benefits: Children really love this sort of activity. They enjoy the sense of protection and enclosure, then they love the feeling of breaking through and being welcomed out of the egg. It seems most useful from the age of about two-and-a-half or three, when many children struggle with the ideas of whether they are a big girl or a little girl, a big boy or a little boy. They may ask to do this activity a lot at a certain age, then lose interest or return to it later. One five-year-old literally grew out of it when he asked to try it again and found his body wouldn't fit any more!

Psychologists in the 1960s, trained in bringing up rats rather than children, advocated 'time out', which meant putting a child in the bathroom or bedroom to cool off. This has some advantages, especially in the area of safety. *It is far better to shut a child in another room*, and give both of you time to cool off, than risk hitting them while you are angry. Time out has saved many children's lives and many parents' sanity.

However, many parents tell us that time out doesn't work for long and the child soon has to go back there again. They may have a good time in their bedroom, which in most homes resembles a Christmas catalogue of toys, so there is no real advantage. Or they will continue their tantrum in there, destroying everything in sight, which returns the problem to you. Or they will escape through the window. And you can't take a time-out room with you when you travel.

The problem with time out is that it doesn't necessarily change anything. A child needs to do some thinking and changing, if the discipline is to work. There is a conversation you need to have with the child (or else the same problem will just happen again the next day). It should go something like this:

What were you doing wrong?
Nothing.
Have a think about it.
Petie took my truck.
Yes. But what did you do wrong?
I didn't hit him hard.
But you did hit him.
Well, yes.
What is the rule about that?
Don't hit.
So what should you have done?
I don't know.
Were you angry?
Yes.
You should have told him in a loud voice, 'Don't take my truck, I want it.'
Oh.
So will you do that next time?
Yes.
Okay, you worked that out really well. I'll be watching to see you get it right.

Maybe they will, maybe they won't. There is a lot of repetition in parenting. Next time, though, you will keep them standing there longer. Child-

ren are uncomfortable standing still and this is the motivation to get on with fixing the problem. As soon as they act reasonably, they are out of there in a flash.

Here's an example with little Darrel, who is two-and-a-half and has had a long play period with his blocks.

Darrel, please pick up the blocks and put them in the box. (Darrel ignores this.) Darrel, do it now. Pick up the blocks.

No.

(Mother comes over and squats beside Darrel at eye level, gets his attention and speaks firmly.) NOW.

(Darrel throws a block across the room and starts crying.)

(His mother picks him up and carries him to the corner, where she holds him.) You will be here in the corner until you finish crying and are ready to pick up the blocks. (Five minutes of squirming and crying as his mother holds him firmly and calms her own body by breathing more slowly.)

(Finally, he stands and is still.)

Are you ready now?

I want to go and see Daddy.

You can go and see Daddy when we've finished here. What do you have to do first?

Pick up the blocks.

Are you ready to do that now?

Yes.

Okay, come and do it. (She stands by and points out some he has missed. Once he has finished, she gives him a quick cuddle.) That's fine, you did that really well. Off you go and see Daddy now.

At this age, children are learning to co-operate, which means letting go of some of their wants, some of the time. This doesn't come easily. They will try all kinds of lurks as they get older. 'You don't love me.' 'You don't understand.' 'I want to do a wee.' 'I feel sick.' Or they will say: 'I'm sorry' and do it again in five minutes time. Congratulate yourself on having a creative and intelligent child, then be firm all over again and they will soon get the message.

This method of discipline we call *Stand and Think*. It soon becomes a familiar ritual and no big deal. It is good to establish a place where the child has to stand. In spite of the connotations from the old days of schoolrooms and dunce's caps, we recommend a spot in a corner of the

Tantrum management:

1. Stop the action — restrain your child if necessary. Use firm holding without hurting.

2. Be clear — tell them this is not OK and explain that they need to use words and deal with you.

3. Don't reinforce the problem by giving them what they were throwing a tantrum to get.

4. Come to an understanding and agreement on how they could express their feelings better in future.

room, facing the wall. 'Go to the corner' becomes a tough and unarguable order and most children will do this if they know you mean it.

'Difficult' children, who have accidentally been conditioned into bad patterns, may need to be physically restrained until they realise that they have to stand still and think. You simply hold them firmly (without hurting) until they stand there unassisted. When they stand straight and still, tell them that they can be out of there as soon as they co-operate, which means saying or doing what they are supposed to. Preferably, they should tell you first what they will do; even when little, they can manage a few words to indicate they have got the message.

Holding your child in the corner might seem harsh, but what is the alternative? In the past, it was hitting — used by 70 per cent of parents routinely. Hitting is frightening, ineffective and cruel, and generally results in worse behaviour in the long run. If you use 'time out', that is fine, but you should still bring the child back to the room and have the conversation that you would in the corner, before resuming play. Otherwise, nothing may have changed.

Discipline is about learning to think things through and changing your behaviour.

Remember that the point is *not* to embarrass or shame a child, so be judicious about using it where it could have this effect. We have used Stand and Think in front of friends and family members, but only because they have used the same method and our child has seen theirs go to the corner, too. We have used the corner in a restaurant, but it was an unobtrusive one; others have stopped their car, pulled off the road to a safe spot and stood a child facing the open door to allow them to resolve a problem before continuing the journey.

Now back to Donald and his mother in the lounge room:

I told you to come back and you kept running away.
I didn't hear you.
I don't believe that. I'm very angry about that and the cake you squashed on the floor.
I'm sorry.
Well, I'm not sure you really are sorry. Stand there some more until I feel better.
(Donald stands and shuffles a bit, and looks over his shoulder. After a minute, his shoulders drop and he looks more settled.)
Now, what are you going to do differently?
I'll do what you tell me first time.
Good. Now come and clean up the cake.

Teaching children to be helpful

Children start by copying, trying to do things for themselves, then wanting to do things for others. Even a two-year-old can put their blocks back in the basket. As they grow, we can easily and naturally encourage them to hang up their towel, take their bowls to the sink, shut drawers, clean up spills etc.

The first 'job' of children is to have fun and, luckily, most are highly qualified. Some are better at it than others — four-year-old Brendan's mother told us: 'He just loves to play. He will play with anything. Give him two rocks and a stick, and he is in heaven.'

Happiness grows naturally. Babies who are loved and cared for will take pleasure in simply *being*. As they grow and become physically capable, they will automatically learn the pleasure of *doing*.

Kids start their learning by *copying* the things you do for them. A six-month-old baby will try to feed you their soggy toast. A toddler will bring you a 'tup of tea' (a toy cup filled with sand). They will pick up things you dropped: 'Here yar, Mum.' Soon they *demand* to help and to be self-

reliant: 'Me do it by self.' They will put their gumboots on back to front and defiantly try to walk in them, rather than seek help, and squeal if you try to speed up their buttoning. They also copy older children, conscientiously trying to be just like the big kids — a mixed blessing, indeed.

At first, we can help our children to do things for themselves — from holding their own cup to eating, dressing, toileting and so on. Then they will start to learn to do things *for others*. To begin with, teach them simple things, such as:
● Being gentle when they play with you.
● Picking up things.
● Being polite, saying 'thank you' and 'please', saying 'hello' and 'goodbye'.

As they grow, the tasks can become more advanced, such as making a bed or negotiating a

Imagination and exercise games

Clean washing

This is great for amusing a child when you are busy — maybe while you are ironing and have a basket of clean washing waiting to be ironed or folded. Tip it out on a clear area of floor, take off the child's shoes and let them play. Explain that it is a pile of leaves and they are the wind. They can rush in, tumble around in the pile, throw clothes in the air and roll about. Or maybe it's a little hill and your child is a rabbit making a burrow, a crab digging into the sand to hide from birds and so on. Roll up a pair of socks and the child can become a kitten, pouncing on it and rolling it.

Feed the ants

If your place is like ours, there is usually no difficulty in finding ants in the yard. Your toddler can sprinkle a few grains of sugar near them, then watch them carry the sugar and walk all over each other. The child can also track them carrying their booty back to the nest. This can take up lots of time and encourages observation skills.

Painting without paints

Sometimes you can find paint substitutes in the pantry — try beetroot juice, soy sauce, tomato sauce, Vegemite. This stimulates all the senses and is best done outside, wearing an old smock (some of these 'paints' are very permanent).

Drawings with flour

Sprinkle flour on a tray or child's table. Invite them to make pictures by drawing in the flour with dry fingers. Combs, leaves and so on can create special effects, too. As each picture is finished, your child can smooth the flour, ready for the next creation. A sifter can be used to cover the last drawing. The flour can also be piled up to make little hills, garden walls, paths, roads and so on.

conflict with another child. We all learn to work and, along with it, we learn a cheery or grumpy disposition towards that work. It's in the toddler years that the foundations are laid.

One woman in her 50s told us this story: 'When we were kids in the '40s, times were tough and my parents had to really work hard with six children and not much money to go around. I was amazed as an adult to discover that you could enjoy the exhilaration of hard work. Looking at my parents now, in their retirement years, I realise that they actually thrive on hard work. Perhaps it's a habit of a lifetime, but they love to be active. I can't keep up with them.'

Taking pleasure in working

Here are some guidelines:

● Keep the jobs simple and rewarding. For example, two-year-olds can pick up their toys and pack them away before bed.

● Show enthusiasm and praise them at first. 'That's a good job.' 'That was very clever.' 'Doesn't the floor look nice?' 'All the toys are safe in the box now.' Eventually, all you'll need to say is: 'Okay, it's bedtime', comfortably expecting the job will be done, then simply accepting that it has been. It's important not to set up an 'escalating rewards' problem.

Praise is given initially so the child feels good. Eventually, they will gain satisfaction from being competent and contributing to everyone's well-being. You will know this in your own experience: it's nice to be praised and there is also the inner satisfaction of knowing what to do — fixing a flat tyre in the bush, for instance; you're

just glad you can do it. It's okay to say things like: 'We all help each other in this family' and: 'We all like living in a clean and tidy house.'

For children from about the age of three, we recommend the movie *Mary Poppins*. Many of us have fond memories of this film which is full of messages about lovingly taking care of children and, at the same time, helping them to be tidy and helpful. You will hear the songs that say: 'For every job that must be done, there is an element of fun' and: 'A spoonful of sugar helps the medicine go down.' Children can (and often spontaneously do) sing these songs as they work. Another fun working song from *Snow White* is 'Hi ho, hi ho, it's off to work we go'.

Good jobs for kids

Here are some examples of first jobs (from two years of age):

- Put away toys at bedtime.
- Empty small wastepaper bin.
- Take plates to the sink after a meal.
- Hang up towel after the bath.
- Put dirty clothes in hamper.
- Tip water into dog's bowl.
- Put clothes pegs into the holder.
- Use dustpan and brush to sweep up.

You can pick any of these or something that you think is more suited to your child.

You will have to explain the job, show your child how to do it the first time, help and do it with them if needed, supervise, encourage and remind them, and still keep it light and pleasant. You will soon see that this is not aimed at making life easy for the parent in the short term. Teaching kids takes energy, but it's a beautiful gift, too, and a *real* way to build self-esteem which praise and adulation alone can never do. Self-esteem comes, eventually, from competence — knowing you can do things well.

Specially for three-year-olds

This is where it becomes fun. It's the age of, one day: 'Let me help, Mummy' and the next day: 'No, I won't do it!' Look on the bright side — this just goes to prove that your child is developing normally, learning to think, behave and feel independently. They are getting to know their changing feelings. They are also starting to test out 'who's in charge around here?' And at this age, their independence can be a real plus for you. For instance:

The sensuous child
(a special note about three- to four-year-olds)

Experienced parents have noticed that, around the age of three or four, children often show heightened sensual awareness. Parents can feel confused and worried when their son or daughter exhibits behaviour which can even look seductive. Parents have often told us they observed:

- Little girls putting beads or other objects into their vaginas and enjoying the feeling as they walk around.
- Children wanting privacy in the toilet, while they experiment with their faeces.
- Children rubbing their genitals against a parent's body during play.
- The classic case of children playing doctors inside a cupboard with another child.

Sandra, 32 'One morning, when we were having a cuddle in bed, my four-year-old son got on top of me and was very smoochy, and said in a seductive kind of voice, "We're making love, aren't we, Mummy?" (He has a book about how babies are made, so I knew where the concept had come from.) I was really shocked, but put him down off the bed and said, "No, we're not; only grown-ups make love." I tried to make it firm, but not too harsh. He went off to play and seemed happy enough. My husband and I made a practice of getting up in the mornings and sitting with our son on the couch, reading or talking, for our close time, instead of being in the bed. After a while, we went back to normal behaviour and the problem passed.'

This seems to be a brief phase, if it is handled matter of factly, by redirecting them to other forms of play.

- Your three-year-old can tell you when and where they feel sick or are hurting, accurately naming the parts of their body.
- They can share and take turns with toys.
- They can understand simple reasons. 'I can't let you go up on that slide; it's too high for me to hold on to you.' 'Nana asked us to come to her house tomorrow — she's busy today.' 'If you put your bowl up on the table, the dog won't get it (again).' 'When you've finished your sandwich, you çan have a drink.' 'This machine is not a toy for playing with; come and we'll find a toy.'

The jobs you choose for this age group should never be backbreaking, frustratingly difficult, totally inconvenient or excruciatingly painful to perform, even though they may try to convince you that's exactly what they are! Remember that

Quiet time

Once, most human beings lived in villages and on farms, and the atmosphere was quiet, reflective, with plenty of time for solitude and exposure to nature. When it was dark, they slept. Music and sound were made naturally or there was quiet. As parents, we certainly appreciate this idea, but children need it, too (although they may not realise it). Explain to your child that this is their quiet time. The length can vary from two to 15 minutes, depending on the age of the child. Explain that it is not a punishment and they will soon start to enjoy it. They are not to play, talk or walk around. A child can sit somewhere pleasant — on a bed looking out to the garden, on a couch by the window, on a chair in a sunny spot.

Instruct them in how to notice all of their sensations — for example, what can they feel touching pillows, a chair, clothes? What can they smell? Or taste in their mouth? Can they hear any sounds, like birds, the wind, traffic, breathing? What sensations can they feel on the inside of their body? Have them look at their surroundings, then pick something to study in detail. They can then close their eyes and imagine seeing inside their body, hearing, tasting and smelling, inside as well as outside.

The first few times, take the child through all of these steps and soon they will be able to do them without help. This can be done routinely once or twice a day, or if the child needs to be settled down during a busy day. It becomes a lifelong skill which is useful to children when they are upset for some reason, such as starting school, visiting the dentist or dealing with teasing.

you've chosen tasks which are simple and no big deal, and that's the way you want your child to treat them. This is the time for learning to follow reasonable instructions, without hassling, feeling bad, arguing or whingeing. There *are* times when jobs can be negotiated or changed because a child has objections.

For example, Steve needed our four-and-a-half-year-old's help to turn open a valve on our diesel water pump, while he cranked it to start. It was a hot day and the youngster refused to come and do it. Steve was about to give him a blast and order him to do it, but instead he softened and asked: 'Why not?' The little boy explained very clearly that the diesel fumes were smelly and he didn't like them. He and Steve waited at a distance for five minutes for the fumes to clear, then started the engine without a hitch. They came home holding hands, looking like proud and successful men.

Teaching children about getting the job done brings up all kinds of important lessons, such as:

● Holding a person to their word.
● Trust.
● Responsibility.
● Honesty.
● Being prompt.
● Remembering.
● Caring about others as well as yourself.

Be relaxed and happy as these questions start to surface. As you supervise your smart three- or four-year-old in their tasks, remember that these issues need to be talked out and learned as they are getting older and ready for school. Help them to think it through by giving them practical examples. For instance, a four-year-old who says: 'I've forgotten to feed the cat' needs to think through why we bother to feed cats. A creative mother we know, when it came to tea time, dished up food for everyone except the child and said: 'Oh, I've forgotten about you, I'll feed you tomorrow' (just like the cat had to wait). She smiled knowingly, then gave the child some tea.

He looked thirsty...

Here are some possible jobs for three- to four-year olds:

● Set the table. Count how many people, placemats and pieces of cutlery are required, in the right places on the table. We used a game: *knife* rhymes with *right*, and *right* is the hand you *write* with (luckily, we're all right handers).
● After the evening meal, scrape scraps into compost bin, put their own plate and cutlery on the bench. Wipe placemats with a cloth. Put them in the cupboard.
● Replace the toilet rolls.

- Feed the cat or dog with food from a cup (later learning to open the can as well).

Sometimes parents designate a particular day of the week — usually Saturday or Sunday — as their *children's regular jobs day*. Others give each child one job per day. Routine daily self-help chores can include:

- Taking off pyjamas and putting them in the right place.
- Getting dressed.
- Doing up buttons and zips.
- Hair and teeth brushing.

These are general ideas only and need to be varied with your child's age and capabilities. Each child is different and there are no comparisons. You will be sensitive to your child's own timing. When they are ready to try something new, there should be no pressure or need to hurry them. They don't have to grow up too fast.

By the age of about four or five, it's good for your child to learn about money. Some parents start to give pocket money for doing jobs for the family; others give it as a right. You might try a combination and find out how you and your child feel about it — a basic wage, plus bonuses. Young children don't need, and shouldn't have, a lot of money to spend. They need to develop a sense of value which comes partly from shortages. A small amount is an interest, and encourages counting, figuring out what they most want, waiting and saving, and *understanding why parents go to work.*

Responsibility — taking it slowly

Be careful not to burden children with responsibilities. Err on the side of simplicity when assigning tasks or asking for their help, as you can always build up to more complex jobs. It's asking for disappointment all round to give kids responsibilities which include precious, expensive or breakable objects. They just don't have the necessary co-ordination yet.

It is also important that youngsters should never be made responsible for other children. You could ask a five-year-old to play with a one-year-old while you go to the kitchen to wash up, as you would have a clear idea of the five-year-old's usual actions towards the baby, and the baby's likely activities, as well as the safety of the room in which you have left them. And you are likely to be within earshot. But know that it is the risk *you* take.

Fun with numbers

Start with the smallest numbers and relate them to things your child knows. For example, when putting on their socks, count them — one-two, two shoes; putting on their jumper — one arm, two arms. When you give them pieces of fruit, count them out as you put them on the plate — one, two, three, four.

Ask questions relating to their body, so they can look and feel to find the answer. How many fingers are on your hand? How many ears do you have? Do this in a playful way — on car trips or in the bath.

You may need to convince yourself that numbers are fun. It helps if you believe that maths is really easy when you know how. Sometimes, as the child is growing up and starts to try bigger sums, we can make the mistake of giving them the impression that these are harder. They might even say, 'No, not hard ones, Mum, give me easy numbers.' Tell them they are all easy; they are just different. The trick is to find the easy way.

You can add up in hundreds, you know.
No, I can't!
Yes — 100 plus 100 is 200. You see — one plus one is two. You can add one plus one, can't you?
Yep!
Now you can add thousands. Now millions. Now trillions!
(Kids love this feeling of power.)

While you are driving in the car, a five-year-old will often enjoy answering funny questions. How many legs do two dogs have? Three cows? If we put 10 eggs on Grandpa's chair, how many will there be after he sits on them? Ten? Or just one big mess? If I put four chocolates and two artichokes on a plate for morning tea, how many would be left for me and how many would you take?

At the supermarket, give your child a shopping bag and ask them to collect four oranges for you. There are dozens of ways you can bring numbers, fractions, dividing and so on into your day-to-day activities together.

This incident happened many years ago. Four-year-old Alice was left in charge of her little sister Meg, aged 18 months, while her mother went to hang out the washing. To keep her precious dolls out of reach of the baby, Alice climbed up and put them on a bookshelf. The little child clambered up after them, on to the first shelf, dislodging a heavy potplant which landed on her head, as she and it fell to the floor. She wasn't badly hurt but, if she had been, there would have been

Look what I can do!

two damaged children — one with a physical injury, the other with a huge guilt problem.

Four-year-olds are not capable of foreseeing all the possibilities that adults can. They act by impulse, rather than intention, and the impulse to fix a problem can be even more damaging than the original problem. It is our responsibility as parents not to expose them to the potential of lifelong guilt.

Kids can easily feel over-responsible, so keep a sense of proportion. We meet many children who are distressed by feeling *too* responsible, especially when there is stress in the family — death, illness or marriage breakup. Children at this age are developing compassion and have a lot of intuition about things which they don't yet understand in words. They *want* to help.

A three-year-old picks some flowers and takes them to an old lady in the park. You can see the old lady is very moved by this — how did the child know she was a person who 'needed' this gesture?

While parents are having a heated argument, their child comes in and stands between them. 'I've got a better idea,' he says earnestly, using the same words they use to mediate in *his* fights with his friends. While this is 'cute', it clearly shows how children can take on the burden of things which should not be their problem. Parents need to say, 'We are sorting something out. We will figure it out. You don't need to worry about it. Go and find something to play with.' The child may still worry, but knows now that it's nothing to do with him.

Similarly, children should never be told that they 'make Mummy sick', 'made Daddy leave', 'are a worry to Grandma' or 'have to be Mummy's big man now'. While children do have a need to know what is going on, and not be shielded from facts of life, like death, sickness and departures, be careful not to burden them with adult responsibilities.

In conclusion...

The great thing about this age group is their emerging personhood. You have a companion and friend. While we've emphasised the discipline and teaching aspects, much of the time spent with them is delightful, laughter-filled and interesting. At this stage, you can already see the future person emerging. Enjoy their company; it's a brief but beautiful time.

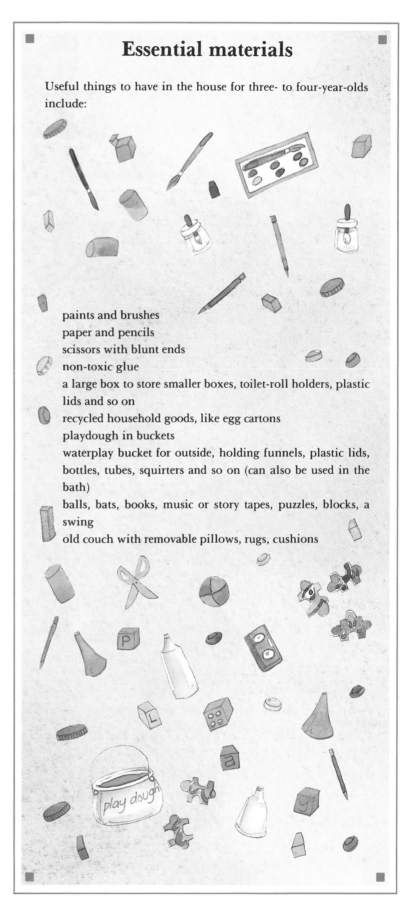

Essential materials

Useful things to have in the house for three- to four-year-olds include:

paints and brushes
paper and pencils
scissors with blunt ends
non-toxic glue
a large box to store smaller boxes, toilet-roll holders, plastic lids and so on
recycled household goods, like egg cartons
playdough in buckets
waterplay bucket for outside, holding funnels, plastic lids, bottles, tubes, squirters and so on (can also be used in the bath)
balls, bats, books, music or story tapes, puzzles, blocks, a swing
old couch with removable pillows, rugs, cushions

Fathers
— the return of the missing ingredient in parenting

by Steve Biddulph

Being a confident dad

One American study revealed that fathers spent 6 minutes per day with their children. Many fathers today are not happy with this. While their hard work outside the home is an expression of their love and devotion, fathers are claiming their relationships with their children too. Fathers are more willing to take the nurturing role and give it the time and energy that this takes.

The re-discovery of fathering is the most exciting thing I've seen in 20 years of working with families. Fathers have always cared about their children, but often it has been from a distance. Working hard to support the family, and feeling less able than a woman to care for children, kept the fathers of the '50s and '60s remote and unsure of how to get close to their kids.

'Hold on, though,' I can hear you saying, 'these days it's different. Lots of men are very involved with their children.' Well, yes and no. It has become fashionable for dads to be present at the birth, mind the children, get up to help with night feeds and so on. This is great and everyone benefits. But it has still been a secondary role, a kind of helpmate — all very Sensitive New Age Guy-ish, and still not the whole story of fathering.

Being a father doesn't only mean being helpful and *nice*. Rather, it means bringing something different to the whole equation. We're starting to realise that dads add a healthy, masculine influence to a family, if they can get over their insecurity. Especially when they have children to care for, women don't want a man who is a bully, but they don't want a wimp either. They want some-

one who is confident in his manhood — in the living room, as well as the bedroom. A man who is at ease with himself, and doesn't hide from getting involved, giving his opinion and discussing how to solve the day-to-day problems that children bring.

HOW ARE FATHERS DIFFERENT?

Men play differently with children. They disrupt and energise and activate children. This can be a bit of a nuisance when mothers are trying to calm them down but, if you can get the timing right, it's great for kids' development.

Fathers, especially, delight in taking the children out and exhausting them. An hour at the park or leisure centre works wonders. One dad I knew found the only way to make his baby son sleep was to walk with him over a shoulder through the streets at night. Another took his baby for drives in the car. For safety, they went round and round the block, and were reported to the police!

Dads have a different perspective. Especially when they come home after a day at work, fathers can sometimes see a need and meet it, when a mother is so up to her neck in babies that she can no longer think straight. For instance, they can take the family out to tea, bring home take-aways or just suggest, 'Let's leave the place untidy and forget it.' (Or, better still, clean it up while the mother sleeps.)

Dads can be good at discipline. Fathers have to learn to be strong and firm, without being hard or mean. They should never hit or abuse their children, nor be cruel or sarcastic. Once they are confident that they have struck the right balance, discipline comes more naturally and easily to them. Mothers can relax because they know their partner will back them up and they are not on their own with difficult kids. Women, especially single mothers who *have* to do it alone, can discipline children, too. But it takes incredible energy.

Dads sometimes cop out of discipline and even side with the children, becoming the proverbial 'soft touch'. In doing so, they undermine their partner and make her feel like a nagger who is hard just for the sake of it. Yuck! Fathers should

back up their partners and, if anything, be the one who is slightly more demanding of the kids. Women are happiest when they can rest in the strength and energy their partners bring to the family scene, and know that it is done safely, too.

THE STAGES OF FATHERING

When your partner is pregnant

You can have a lot of feelings during pregnancy. Mostly, if you let yourself, you will feel tender and protective, even in some awe of your partner's ability to perform this miracle. But some fathers-to-be seem to freak out. The fact that, according to one study, 25 per cent of all wife-bashing takes place while women are pregnant indicates that something goes badly wrong in the psyche of some men at this time. Be alert to feelings of jealousy or threat.

I feel that something has come between us...

Your partner's interest in sex will swing widely during pregnancy — from not at all to highly motivated. If you think that sex is like beer in the fridge for you to take when you feel like it, grow up! Real men make love with their partners by mutual seduction, kindness, care and respect. If her hormones are changing or her body is uncomfortable, respect her feelings. At the same time, respect your own feelings and don't give up too easily if you want to win her over. There are ways to gain mutual satisfaction other than intercourse (outercourse, for instance!).

Sometimes men take their partner's sexual responsiveness as an indication of whether they are loved or not. They get surly and sulky if she is

Tests of strength

(especially good for dads)

The invitation to begin this game is often given by children, without them realising it. They will start insisting: 'I'm the biggest in this family', 'I know what's best', 'I know more than you do', 'I'm in charge around here.' Whereby the parent proceeds to pin the child to the floor, using strength without hurting them (adjust your grip if the child complains that it hurts). This is always done playfully, with the aim of the child happily, if reluctantly, surrendering.

We find that children giggle all the way through this, giving a sure sign that they were 'asking' for a show of strength and vigour from you. Keep going until they acknowledge that: 'You know more than I do' or: 'You are in charge.' You'll also notice, when they stand up, that they look refreshed and not defeated. A variation for littlies is father/son tyrannosaurus rex battles.

Benefits: There are times in a child's growing, when they are feeling their strength and independence, but can get an exaggerated idea of it. They really thrive on testing themselves against you. Unconsciously, they want/need to feel secure — to know at a physical level you are not a pushover. Sometimes a carefully controlled physical 'play battle' does more good than a thousand words. Even adolescents love a good arm wrestle or a rough and tumble. Fathers are best equipped for this work, but mothers can do it, too.

Mothers we know have naturally found their own variations of this game. One reported the benefits of actually sitting on top of her teenage daughter, to show that she 'would so' be able to stop her going out that night. This ended in hilarity. Younger children also learn from 'playfights' how to use strength in play, without hurting themselves or their playmates. If they get too rough, stop, point this out, then start again, so they can get it right.

not interested. They think that their partner is like their mother — the source of their well-being. Your penis isn't the only key to feeling loved. And you won't die if you can't make love for a month or two. I swear!

As birth approaches

It's natural for many of us to feel scared for our partner as the time for the birth gets close. Part of this is that we want to protect her, yet can't do a great deal. We may feel, at best, a helpful supporter, but just being there is exactly what is required of us. Be sure that you don't get excluded by pushy hospital staff. In fact, look for a birth place which clearly welcomes partners and includes them in the birthing process — at home, in a birth centre or hospital, or during a caesarean operation.

I got very panicky in my partner's fifth month of pregnancy and discovered this had its origins way back in my childhood. When my mother was pregnant with my younger sister, she disappeared to hospital (I didn't even know she was pregnant) and was in danger of dying. (This was 1956 and I was three years old.) Now my partner was pregnant, part of my unconscious mind was mixing her up with my mother back then. I was irrationally fearful that she would (1) disappear, and (2) die and never come back. It was enormously helpful to realise this and separate fact from fiction.

These days, birth is very safe, particularly for the mother. In our case, I was able to handle being present at the caesarean operation and was far too excited to faint. I took our son straight into my arms and felt great.

When the baby arrives

This is the time when it all gets practical. Snatching sleep. Changing nappies. Accumulating dishes in the bedroom because you are too tired to carry them back to the kitchen. This is when mothers-in-law miraculously become beautiful angels of mercy, whom you embrace gratefully at the front door as they bring casseroles and offer to let you go out for the evening.

It's possible you will feel jealous that your baby has replaced you, that your partner is in love with an 8 lb Casanova. This is particularly the case if you are a 12 st baby! Seriously, though, it helps to talk with your partner and get her reassurance that you have her love and appre-

---

A restful environment

People respond to atmosphere. A noisy, harsh atmosphere makes us hurried and tense. That's why there are bright lights in supermarkets and candles in restaurants. You can create an atmosphere in your home, as well as within your child and within yourself. If you notice you are sick of loud noises, agitation, busyness, be sure to do something about it. To encourage restfulness and softness:

● Cut down stimuli. Turn TV and radio off. Use gentle music, or none. Close the curtains; light candles, if you wish.
● Have a glass of wine or cup of tea. Calming drinks for children include warm milk, Horlicks and chamomile tea.
● Have a slow bath together. After the bath, spend some time holding, talking gently or singing, with your child wrapped in a warm dressing gown.

---

ciation, if not much of her time. The first year is tough but, gradually, you get her back. You will sometimes both feel that you are more like shift-workers than lovers. Build in little reminders that you have a romantic view of your partner, even though she feels like a prize milk cow.

Don't be demanding — some men we know have left their marriages because they couldn't handle the competition. At the same time, some women forget they have a partner who matters, too, as they fall head over heels into baby bliss. (Some mothers 'hide' behind their infant and comfort themselves with a baby's love, rather than deal with the demands and complexities of nurturing their adult relationship. Both partners have to stay committed to feeding and caring for their relationship, so that it can thrive.) Remind her, pleasantly, that you are still there and you are the one who knows how to give, while babies mostly take.

The toddler years

With toddlers, fathering often means backing up your partner in matters of discipline. Standing your child in the corner and talking tough with them. Making sure they understand that they must change their behaviour. Not hiding behind the newspaper or wandering off in the shopping mall, so that your partner has to do the tough stuff with the little ones.

Geoff, 39 'My daughter of 19 months has just had her first "stand in the corner till you get

Developing common interests is a way to become and stay friends with your children. Then spending time together is pleasurable. You can talk while you play, as well as teach important values like "relax and enjoy yourself", and "sportsmanship". Fun, not performance, is the goal.

Stop on command

A child's ability to stop abruptly, on command, can be vitally important. Every parent has needed to call a child to halt as they run towards traffic or other unseen danger. Starting as a game, this can be practised whenever it occurs to you or whenever you notice that the lesson needs reinforcing.

With an infant, you begin with any fun thing they are doing. Join in with them, then say 'stop' and stop them with your hands. For example, in the bath, or pool, both of you slap the water — splash splash splash — then say 'stop', holding their hands still. Repeat the game. Say 'good stopping', when they do it by themselves. You could swing them around you and say 'stop', then swing them until they say 'stop' and you obey. Later, they can run on the spot, until you say 'stop'. Build up to having them stop when they are running forwards.

With older children, include an explanation of its importance. You can also correct them if they are slow in responding, by instructing them: 'When I say "stop", you should do it straight away. Start again and show me how you do it straight away. That's right.'

Benefits: This game helps children learn an automatic reaction that might be lifesaving. By learning in a playful way, with the reward of encouragement, there is built-in pleasure and a feeling of achievement.

If you ever doubt the benefit of a child being able to follow an instruction immediately in a dangerous situation, we recommend the movie *Empire of the Sun*. In the midst of a fleeing crowd in wartime Shanghai, a young boy is told by his mother to hold on to her hand while they make their way through the throng. As they head towards the only safe escape, the boy drops his prized toy, reaches to get it and is swept away in the crowd. He becomes a prisoner of the Japanese and it is years before his mother sees him again. It's a memorable image!

the message'' session. We were surprised how early it started. She played with the electric flex to the TV and, when told not to, grinned and did it again — a sure sign that discipline time had begun! Jenine took her over to the corner of the lounge and kept her there. She (the little one, not Jenine) squealed and yelled and raged, and looked at me for support. So I went and held her there, too. Jenine and I grinned at each other — the terrible twos already! It was about five minutes before our daughter gave up on her anger and stopped hassling. We repeated the instruction — ''hands off electric flexes'' (who knows what a two-year-old understands?) — then stood back and watched her. She walked to the middle of the room, eyed the electric flex, eyed us, then went straight over to her toys to play. We've had a couple of reinforcing times, but nothing so major. Often, just the mention of ''corner'' is enough to get her co-operation.'

I've seen some dads do the opposite and undermine their partners: 'Oh, she's so sweet, don't be so hard on her.' Remember that backing up your partner will mean you can both be more relaxed and positive. You can discuss strategies later, but what kids need from parents is a united front if they are to know where they stand.

TIME IS WHAT COUNTS

Simply spending time with your children might make the biggest difference of all and boys, especially, need fathers. Author Robert Bly believes that boys are genetically programmed to need four or five hours of male input per day. While they can get by on two or three hours, many get 10 minutes, maximum. Modern commuter-career lifestyles can make it very hard to be a good dad.

For thousands of years, boys grew up with their fathers and other males in the home, working together, learning to be men. Girls today learn to be women during the thousands of hours they spend with Mum and with female teachers through primary school. But boys who lack sufficient male contact (and for this read *most of us*) have to just pretend to be men, hoping no one will notice.

Recently, I took a brave step and offered a seminar for fathers only. The bond we forged during that half-day session was very strong, as we admitted how lonely and separate from our fathers most of us felt. The room seemed full with grief — grief which was very healing, as it was shared, but painful to witness and deeply felt. There was a real determination not to cause this kind of pain to our sons, and daughters too.

Dads also help the healthy development of daughters — mostly by the same means as for boys. Girls, too, need to know how to change a tyre, build models, fish, hike, play football and so on. But there is an extra role for the opposite-sex parent, in helping to build their daughter's confidence in herself as a young woman. If they get the balance right, fathers provide a source of admiration and warmth, which gives their daughter self-esteem about her conversation, sense of humour, intelligence, looks and how to interact with males generally. Dad can do this by being interested, admiring, but never flirtatious or in any way sexual. He's a 'safe' male, with whom a girl can learn to be comfortable and confident with men.

WHAT IF YOU ARE A SINGLE FATHER?

There is no point beating around the bush — being a single parent is hard. Single dads find it difficult to be both father and mother, giving tenderness and managing the household, as well as making a living. Children give affection back to us, but the human design is to have an adult partner fuelling your supplies of love.

Take care to keep up adult friendships and have a life of your own. Don't let your children be your only support network; you have to learn not to use single parenthood as a safe retreat from the world. Find adult friends and involve others in the care of your kids. Many single dads tell us they feel lonely and awkward at playgroups and preschool, with all those women around. Enjoy it! Perhaps, as more fathers are doing the care-giving, there will be more inter-dad support everywhere.

If you are separated or divorced and have access to your children, you need to learn to be balanced in your care of them. Resist the temptation to be super-generous and tolerant of bad behaviour, for fear of losing their affection. They will feel most secure if you are firm and don't allow them to play you off. Your children will always need you and want to know about you as their real

---

Animals and feelings

Pets have many benefits for children. The (slightly idealistic) idea of learning responsibility through caring for a pet is well known. This activity is more specific.

Little children need help to learn to read the body language of animals they meet. It's especially helpful to show a child the signs which tell when a cat or dog is unhappy (that is, losing patience). When a cat flicks her tail, puts her ears down or starts to meow, she might be angry and could scratch or bite. When you go near the dog's food, and he starts to growl and flattens his ears, that might mean he is warning you to stay back. It is his food and he is protecting it.

Your child will be able to identify with this. An explanation will result in the child being confident around animals, rather than unnecessarily scared. At the same time, they will avoid unhappy encounters through bad timing. Very young children can be taught to pat and stroke animals gently, instead of grabbing or pulling. Show them and hold their hand to demonstrate. They will see the dog wag its tail or the cat purr. Tell them, 'See, you have made him happy.'

---

father, even if they have a stepfather. Don't disappear from the scene, even though it is sometimes hard not to. Get on with your life and be happy; this will mean they can approach you comfortably. You will always be their father.

FATHERHOOD AND YOUR CAREER

One danger of all this fathering stuff is that you can have the male equivalent of the Superwoman syndrome — the career success/super stud/super dad triangle which could give you a heart attack on the spot. Fatherhood is the time to become mellow, and learn to accept moderation and balance in all your roles. If possible, it's a good idea to relax in your job for a while. You have hit the slow track.

John, 27 'You drag yourself out of the baby-struck household, miraculously cleaned up and tidied, like a lotus rising out of the stinking swamp. As you're about to leave, your wife hands you the baby to cuddle for a minute. You arrive at work, immaculate in your

Reading preparation

Babies and children love having stories read to them. Find books which *you* enjoy, with pictures that are pleasant for you to look at five hundred times! Keep looking for new books; use libraries or shop at jumble sales and markets, where you can go home with a shopping bag full of books for a couple of pounds.

Let them see you reading. They'll notice how you concentrate and become engrossed in your magazine, newspaper or book; how you sometimes laugh or talk about a part of the book with others. You can tell them what your book is about and that they can read it one day, too.

Play the 'my word' game. Once a day, ask the child to choose something in the house. Make a sign with that word clearly printed on it and let them stick it to the object. After a week, collect the signs and see if the child can return them to the right places. To help a younger child, you can draw the object on the back of the sign as a clue.

Play 'word snap'. Together, choose the names of people your child likes, then make pairs of cards with these names printed on them. Shuffle the cards and deal equal numbers to you and your child. First, the child puts one down, then you put one of yours next to it. Does it match? Yes. 'Snap!' The first one to see the match and say 'snap' wins. You can also spread out the cards face up and together find the ones which are the same.

Invent rhyme and rhythm games. Reading is about enjoying words. As you walk together, get the rhythm going. 'We are... walking... up the ... hill. Peter... is the... fastest... one. I am... catching... up with him.' Make funny rhyming words — for example, using Peter's name. 'Peter, neater, sweeter, cheater, meet her.'

Leave notes. In the morning, the child finds a large, simple note on the floor of the bedroom. It includes signs or drawings to give a clue to the message. 'Hello' (picture person waving) 'I love you' (heart). 'Boo' (surround with dots). The signs become more challenging as the child gets older — 'Good morning, come to our bed at...' (picture of clock with hands pointing to 8 o'clock).

dark suit, and, as you finish your meeting, someone points out that the baby has burped down your back, leaving a mark like the world's biggest seagull has pooped on you. Welcome to the real world!'

You go away for three days (a work trip you can't get out of) and find yourself in airports and shopping malls envying other people's babies, wondering if you would be arrested if you gave a passing toddler a quick hug. You've joined the worldwide league of dads, men who have lost their competitive edge and don't care. Men who have slowed down, eased up, realised what matters and are in for the long haul. Even your view of women will change... 'Hmmm, good hips.' 'Wow, see how she handles that pram.' 'Nice way with the pulverised vegetables.'

This may sound like you are less of a career success; but, in fact, you will become better. You will have compassion, feel more interest and concern for your staff and workmates, and want to do work which improves the human race, instead of just making a quick buck. You might change jobs or move out of the rat race to a more satisfying line of work. Family life will give you depth of understanding of others which will make you good with people, and a deeper and better person all round.

I hope this short, extra section is useful. Fathering is more important than most people realise and we have a lot to learn. Rent the Steve Martin video, *Parenthood*, and you will enjoy some feelings of recognition. Like anything worthwhile, fathering is tough but rewarding. See you at the school gate!

Protecting children from sexual abuse

A child's first line of protection is the quality of everything we do as parents. We don't expose them to danger, are careful who we entrust them to, listen to their feelings and concerns, and teach them to value themselves. These general practices and patterns are usually the best way to ensure children's safety in all aspects of their lives. We can add many specific steps, including the following which were suggested by experienced parents.

● Use the real words. Teach children the proper names for body parts — vagina, vulva, penis, nipples, anus and so on. This gives them more ability to talk about their body and takes away needless mystery.

● Talk the language of feelings. Help children to identify and be able to express what they are feeling — happy, sad, scared, unhappy, angry and so on. They will be better able to talk to you about their feelings when they *do* have a concern.

● Remove fear from your discipline. Use effective discipline which does not involve fear. Don't use physical or verbal threats or abuse; listen to their side in a dispute. This teaches them that they can come to you, even if they feel guilty, and you will listen and not hurt them.

● Teach them the 'stop' rule. In games you play with them and they play with each other, have a rule that anyone can say 'stop' and be respected. Ensure that all players obey that rule. This is very important in letting children know they will be respected and can have time out. (It is also useful for adults who are arguing.) Part two of this rule is that, if they say 'stop' and the other person does not comply, they *must move away* from the game and *get help* from someone older, if necessary.

● Teach and value privacy. Gradually introduce the idea of privacy. Point out that adults don't undress with others around, nor do they touch their genitals in public. Explain that you want them to follow these conventions, too.

● Don't sexualise your children. It is best for young children *not* to witness sex, even on TV. Dress children age-appropriately. Don't joke about young children having 'girlfriends' and 'boyfriends'.

● Abolish secrets. Don't use or have secrets as part of your family life. Children should not be expected to keep things to themselves. Children who are told or threatened by someone that they must 'keep a secret' will know this is wrong and that their parents expect them to tell.

● At any age, children should only stay the night where you know *all* of the family well and when it is clear that no other visitors will be sleeping-over.

● Trust your intuition. Act on your feelings. Often, the only warning of child abuse is an intuition you have about a person or situation, that 'something isn't right'. Even if you have no facts to support you, it's okay to say 'no' to an invitation or situation you don't feel 100 per cent comfortable about.

● Don't push children to be intimate — encourage them to kiss or hug only those people *you* would kiss or hug.

● Go with them into public toilets. We need better and more single-entry toilets, or parent/child toilets, in public places.

● Don't touch their genitals after nappy age. From about the time children are out of nappies (three to four years), no one but themselves should specifically touch their genitals, unless for a medical examination. They can learn to wash and care for their own penis or vagina and, if they have a problem, it is best if they show you, and for them to do the touching, rather than you.

● Be careful with carers. Have *very* high standards about who cares for your children. Make a practice of dropping in unannounced from time to time, even (especially) when this is discouraged.

● Start with yourself and your partner. Adults need contact with and affection from other adults. This saves you from using your children as your sole source.

The preschool year

Questions and answers

A GROUP OF PARENTS SHARE PROBLEMS AND SOLUTIONS

It's a sunny day outside, and windy. A good-natured group of 21 mothers and 12 fathers is looking forward to an afternoon of talking about parenting, sharing problems and solutions, and enjoying adult company and support without the presence of their children. The group is comfortable together, so we dive in at the deep end and ask them: 'What, specifically, do you want to know about kids of preschool age? Let's find out the most common questions.'

Why do they always ask 'why' about everything?
Yes!, exclaim a couple of other parents.
What kind of thing?, we ask.
Why is there air? Why is that lady so fat? Why do cows have legs? That sort of stuff. Does it ever stop?

> **You don't have to read books to learn how to be a parent, but you do have to talk to other parents. You can get a shoulder to cry on, a good idea, a pat on the back, the relief of a good laugh together.**

No!, joke a couple of others. (There is good-natured groaning.)
How can you make children not speak — for a year or two?
Why do they argue so much? They keep wanting to argue every little point. I thought I had them well trained and now they mutiny.
How can I keep them busy?
How much TV should they watch? And computer games—are they good or bad?
My child is turning into a bully. What can I do about it? I yell at him and hit him and it doesn't seem to help.
My boy is a real wimp, he always gets picked on. How can I get him to stand up for himself?
I worry about my daughter being abducted. She is too trusting — should I teach her to be more afraid?
Can I help my kids with learning to read?
What can we do on long car trips?
I hated school when I was a child. How can I get my children ready for school, so that they like it?

Lots of questions, revealing that this is a dynamic and challenging age. It's the age of the mind. Every child is a genius, a swirling, sparkling intelligence, swimming like a dolphin in the ocean of learning. Or a shark, voraciously scouring the world for mental nourishment. *They want answers!*

So we and the group of parents began to talk, exploring the world of the four-year-old. This chapter is based on the afternoon's discussions and input — what a preschool child is like; how to foster their learning; more about discipline; the positive power of arguing; how to delight in the fantasy and imaginative worlds of children; and how to help them build real skills with people and things, so that they go off to school keen and hungry for more which, thankfully, their teachers are paid to provide.

Dealing with all those questions

Sometimes questions have simple answers and kids are happy with them — for example, cows have legs to keep their bodies from catching on the ground. At other times they are on a roll, wanting more, so you can throw it back to them:

Why do you think? To walk around?
But why?
Well, what do cows like?
Grass!
So how do their legs help them?
To get to more grass.

Sometimes questions go in circles. Decide if you want to talk or not. If you're busy, say so — don't get cranky. But remember that they are more open to learning now than later and this is cheap education.

Where does rain come from?
Where do you see it come from?
The sky, but how does it get there?
From clouds.
Where do clouds come from?
The ocean. They blow over the land and drop the rain.
(You can outrun them, too.) *Where do you think the ocean gets its water from?*
(Long pause...) The rain!
Yep.
Dad, do fish pee?

Sometimes (often, in our case) you just *don't know* the answer, so suggest other people they could ask. Be genuine about it — go and find out for them sometimes; they will be most impressed. In our village, there is a very good craftsman, called John Bright. Our son assumes John will know about anything technical. Other people are good with nature and plants. His grandfather knows all about shells, horses and sport.

Separating truth from fantasy
At this time, when fantasy and imagination are blossoming, many and varied are the pretend friends and imaginary adventures. One day, they are showing us 'cat land' or 'snail city' and we are enthusing with them. But next day, when they tell us the snails took the chocolate cake from the fridge, we have to draw the line.

The first time your child lies to you can come as a shock. It's a normal stage; so don't panic, but help them to make a distinction in their own mind about what is real and what is made up.

A young woman in the group offered this example: 'We were at a playgroup picnic and there was a donation box that Shelley was sitting near. I never gave it any thought. On the way home, I saw her playing with a line of small

Gifts of power

When choosing gifts for children, we want them to be re-usable, allow imaginative play, be durable, attractive, interesting, educational and appropriate to their age and skills. Phew! But there is something magical and symbolic in gifts, too.

Occasionally, someone will choose a very special gift which exactly fits your child's needs. It's as if the gift reflects the child's spirit, bringing with it confirmation of the next step the child will take in their development as a person. I call these 'gifts of power'. They may be simple or complex, expensive or cheap, home-made or bought, but they are uniquely appropriate to this child at this time. Here are some examples:

● A small piece of very soft and cuddly blanket or a woolly sheepskin for a two-year-old who is having trouble sleeping.

● A soft, hand-made rag doll to comfort a child who is moving from a cot to a bed.

● Home-made Inspector Gadget outfit (an old coat, equipped with all kinds of hardware store/camping gadgets in the pockets). This was for a child who was introverted, but full of hidden qualities which needed encouraging.

● A busy box for a child who was getting into lots of trouble for being demanding. This helped by redirecting her intelligence and energy into creating things, instead of creating havoc. Any attractive box can be used and filled with craft items, such as glue, pompoms, ribbons, bells, fluff, material offcuts, feathers, clasps, cardboard, scissors, doilies, paper cups, ice-pole sticks, straws, rubber bands and cardboard tubes.

● The *right* book. Everyone remembers a special book from their childhood which they could really relate to. Choosing the right book is a delightful experiment. Books often have a message which is subtly put — for instance, the old Rupert books are all about friendship, and the challenges and joys of playmates. There are good guides to what books are loved by what ages of children but, above all, base your choice on knowing the particular child and what they will find magical and beautiful.

Thinking games

With each activity, adjust the difficulty to match what you think your child can understand. This is a pretend game, in which the parent takes the lead.

Right, we'll play the pretend present game. I've got a present for you. (Parent thinks of something exciting to pretend they have to give the child.)
Okay, thank you.
Now you have to guess what it is. It is big.
Is it a horse?
No, it's very big and round and blue.
A flying saucer?
No, it's also very wet and fun to play in.
A swimming pool!
Yes!

As they grow towards school years their creative genius unfolds before our eyes. If we make a range of activities and equipment available, and stand out of their way, children will choose for themselves according to their own interests — not just what girls or boys are *supposed* to like.

coins, so I asked: "Where did you get them from?" and straight away she answered: "From your purse."

I knew my purse was empty, so I had to make her tell the truth. It was very upsetting.'

Sometimes it's hard in new situations for children to weigh up right and wrong, as temptations (or opportunities) occur. With their new-found powers of explanation, carefully developed by you, they realise they can fabricate explanations after the fact.

Don't let them confuse you. Help them to look back at what they were thinking and feeling at the time. After helping her to be specific, Shelley's mother told her: 'I understand what you are saying — that you wanted the money. I know you

like saving up and it looked like anyone could have it. But you felt it was wrong to take it, because then you pretended it came out of my purse. That's true, isn't it? Do you know who it does belong to? How would it be if someone came and took some out of your money box? Now what can you do to fix it up?'

Shelley went with her mum to give back the money and apologise. Chances are good that Shelley won't make up stories another time — this was fairly uncomfortable for her. But, if she does, she will know that it's possible to get back to the truth and fix things up.

Keep reminding children of the truth in different situations — for example:

I'm as old as Phillip.
No, Phillip is 10 years old, you're four years old.
I know him.
No, you don't know him.
You said I could have an ice-cream today.
No, I didn't.
Well, Dad said I could.
Okay, let's check that out with Dad.
(Or: *So, if we go and ask Dad what happened, what will he say?*)

Encourage owning up, by showing consequences for the lie, while making it clear that it would have been much worse if they hadn't been brave enough to own up. This helps us to be honest in *our* dealings, because children will pick up on the dishonesty and even drop us right in it. Here's an example:

Doing the dishes

Four-year-olds *can* learn to dry up. We suggest positioning a chair, with a towel on its seat, by the sink; the child dries up over the top of this in case they drop crockery.

Start them with saucepans, spoons, plastic utensils, bowls and so on, working up to flat plates which can be placed on the towel-covered seat, wiped, turned over and wiped again. Over the age of five, they can start on glasses and, using our special patting method, knives: place knife on the towelled chair, make a ball with your teatowel and pat the knife dry with the ball-shaped towel. Turn the knife over by the handle and do the other side. (Of course, you will need to stick around to supervise.)

A tired mum had just got her two toddlers and a baby to lie down for a rest and was horrified to see, through her front window, the approach of Mrs Maloney. She just didn't want to talk to this long-winded but kindly old neighbour today. So she whispered to the oldest child who was still awake, 'Shhh, be quiet and go to sleep.' When Mrs Maloney returned later that day, the four-year-old bounced up to her and announced: 'We hid from you before!'

Everyone has stories like these...A new child at school was being introduced to his class. Asked where he was from, he said 'London'. 'And what work does your father do?' (A foolish question at the best of times.) 'Oh, he's into drugs.'

A four-year-old asked his grandma at Sunday lunch: 'Is your neck better now, Gran?' 'Why?' asked the old lady, as the parents stiffened visibly. 'Dad said this morning you had a pain in the neck.' Or something like that...

Fixing mistakes

Mistakes are an important part of life and, if you can't admit to them, you have to pretend you're perfect, which is very hard work. Or you can never try anything new, which is limiting. One of the greatest gifts you can give your kids is the sense that it's okay to make mistakes, as long as they also fix them. This might include:

● Apologising — being willing to admit we were wrong and to say 'sorry'.
● Openness — explaining our intentions and 'where we were coming from'.
● Telling the truth and owning up to our actions.
● Taking responsibility — fixing the damage, paying the cost, and so on.

Janice, 38, walked into her five-year-old son's room to find him quickly pushing a chocolate wrapper under his bed. 'He looked so suspicious,' she told us, 'I knew something was amiss.' It soon became clear he had taken the chocolate while they were at the shops earlier that day.

Richard, I'm really upset about this. Taking without paying is stealing and stealing is wrong. What are you going to do to fix it?
I won't take anything ever again.
That's good. But what about this chocolate bar?
I can't take it back; I've nearly eaten it all.
So what do you think you can do?
I don't know.
Well, you took it without paying for it. They cost about 50p. I think you need to go back to the shop and explain, and give them 50p from your money box.
(Richard went very pale.) *Can you give them the money, Mum?*
No, I didn't take the chocolate. You need to fix this with the shopkeeper. I'll come with you.
Oh...okay.
How about we go now?
Now!?
Yep. You'll feel much better when it's fixed.
(As they drove to the shopping centre, Janice helped Richard figure out what he would say to the shopkeeper.)
How about saying I accidentally took it?
No. That's not true. What is true?
I took it without paying and I'm sorry I did. I want to pay for it now.

Janice also felt a lot better when this was over. The shopkeeper was amused and very co-operative, though he behaved sternly enough for Richard to get the message. Most adults and kids are reasonable, but you need to stand by young children as they fix their mistakes, to make sure they are neither unduly persecuted nor rescued.

Sometimes kids persist in stealing or other unacceptable behaviour when they are having problems, feeling neglected or even suffering abuse. They should still sort out the problem as above, but we need to be alert to what may be the underlying cause. An important question is: what was going on in the child's life when this problem surfaced?

A final point — kids only really learn the skills that we have mastered, so we need to model the behaviour we want in our dealings with them. When we break an agreement or forget a commitment, we should say 'sorry', fix the problem and not use excuses.

Kids keep us honest. We can show them how mistakes can be turned into positive outcomes. The result will be real poise and maturity for us and our children.

LIKEABILITY

Are your children likeable? It's easier to live with pleasant people of any age. If your child has unpleasant habits, they can get in the way of you and other people liking them. Since your aim is to raise a child who can make it in the world, it is okay to do all you can to help them to change. Firstly, though, have a think about whether their behaviour is just a sign of their individuality and is really *your* problem. For instance, creative, talkative, musical, inquisitive and lively kids can be a trial, but you don't want to squash their vitality.

Often, though, a particular habit will clearly be a problem for all and sundry, bringing unfortunate consequences for the child, which you can foresee and they cannot. They are at risk of becoming unlikeable. The parents in our afternoon group had lots of examples and we worked on several with which you might identify.

Dealing with bedwetting
Marg looked like she'd been waiting on the edge of her seat for this chance. 'What about bedwetting?' 'Yes,' added her husband. Their five-year-

Signifying changes

Children have their own achievements. Each birthday signals that a whole year of learning has gone by and that the child is an older and different person from the previous year. Some parents like to spend time with their child, on or after a birthday, going through the child's room and putting away or giving away those things they have outgrown — clothes, toys, books, pictures. (But be careful not to do this with precious or important possessions.)

This clearing out and remaking of their environment helps children to notice changes in themselves and to celebrate their achievements. The freshness and newness of their surroundings helps them to feel fresh and new, too.

Ways in which parents 'signify' their child's growing up can include:
● At an appropriate time, take away or put away 'baby things' (special blanket, for instance).
● Expect and reward dry beds by giving your child a bed of their own.
● Change baby words you have used and remind them to use the proper words. For example, no longer ask: 'Do you want a bowl of yummies?' but: 'Do you want some morning tea?'
● No longer rescue them in their play with another child, now that they have information about how to solve problems. Remind them that they know what to do and send them back to fix it.
● Buy a school bag, even though they are only in nursery.
● Start giving them pocket money and helping them to use it.

Positive discrimination
If you have a baby, it's a good idea to give special privileges to the older child — staying up a little later or doing grown-up things like going to the shops with you while baby is minded. This will send a signal that you value maturity and that being older pays. This way, you won't have two or more children competing to be babylike and it will be fair in the long run, as younger children grow into privileges. But, in the short term, special benefits associated with being older will compensate for the time-consuming nature of the younger children and make the older one feel special and want to be more helpful.

old son, Jason, was still wetting his bed. It was annoying, smelly and worrying, since their other two kids had stopped by the time they were three. Marg and Harry were really 'peed off'!

So, what is your goal?
No more bedwetting.
Put it in the positive. What do you want?
Dry beds.
Good. What do you think might be behind his behaviour?
I think he's just slack. He can't be bothered going to the toilet. (This from Harry.)
Could be. How about you, Margaret — do you agree?
I don't know if he is lazy — it upsets him, too. He cries about it sometimes.

We went on to give some background. The thing we usually check out with any behaviour is: what's normal for this age? Bedwetting is pretty common in five-year-olds. We think about 70 per cent of four-year-olds wet the bed often and 40 per cent of kids of school age still do sometimes.

Other parents piped up: 'Yes, one of ours still does, too.' 'So it's fairly normal, but that doesn't mean you have to put up with it,' we added.

Next, you check other possible causes:

● Is there any physical problem — bladder capacity, muscle problems, urinary tract infection, diabetes? This is your doctor's area, and good to check out first of all. ('We've done all that, ' said Harry.)

● Is there any big stress in his life? Or something he might not have told you about?

● Has he shown that he *can* control it? Does he sometimes have dry beds? Where and when?

● Is there a pay-off? Does he get to see you in the middle of the night, while he doesn't see you much in the day? Who washes the sheets?

We talked around this with Marg and Harry. He was surprised there could be reasons other than just laziness. Marg, however, was feeling like getting tough. Now, it was time for the third step — deciding to act.

The whole group weighed in with things that had worked for them or other people they had heard of, and Marg and Harry added their ideas, too. What we came up with was:

● Visit to toilet before going to bed.

● See a doctor again to double check. Choose a doctor with commonsense who won't make a big deal of it.

● Use a wetness alarm, available from pharmacies.

● Have a good think about whether Jason could have secret worries, from school or elsewhere. Ask about this in a caring and undramatic way. Listen to him and talk to his teacher.

● Leave the light on in the hall and toilet, or a potty near the bed with a night light beside it.

● Consider homeopathic or chiropractic treatment.

● For a few nights, let him sleep on a mattress on the floor beside your bed, so he can wake you if he wants to do a wee. Help and praise him if he wakes you up and gets it right.

● Conversely, don't get involved at all during the night.

● Give rewards for dry nights — stars on a chart towards a zoo trip or an overnight visit to a friend's house.

● Let him know where clean bedding and pyjamas are kept. Don't help with this. It's his job to put wet bedding in a separate bin to be washed. Kids older than six can wash their own. (The reason we don't wet the beds is that it is too much work cleaning up!)

Harry decided to spend time with Jason at bedtime, and to have a talk with him about school and so on. Marg was pleased and decided to follow the other ideas, stop changing the sheets for Jason and have a star chart for his successes, with a reward for five straight nights. The secret is to be creative and keep experimenting.

Sometimes grandparents or friends can help to work out what's going on with a child. It's important that children have close relationships with people other than their parents. They can give encouragement, comfort and a different point of view.

Stimulating the imagination

Hand games

Hold up your pointer finger and have a pretend lasso in the other hand. Make the action of lassoing the finger, then pull on the end of the pretend rope and make your finger bend accordingly. Pull it up, down, over your head, around your neck, under the table and so on. Now hand the end of the pretend rope to your child and let them tug it gently, or say it has come undone and you have to tie it on again.

Stories

You or your child start up a story and take turns in adding to it, as in this example between Jenny, who starts the story, and her mother.

Once there was a witch.
And her name was?
Vera was the witch.
And she had two pockets in her britches.
She had itching powder in one and a frog in the other.

In another story starter, you use the name of the child and their best friend — for example: 'One day, Lewis and Rohan were going for a walk and they came across a box left in the middle of the road...'

Or you can set the story in familiar surroundings — for example: 'One Sunday morning, Dad went outside and saw our old blue pram rocking and shaking, and when he went to look in it he saw...'

Make the stories ridiculous, hilarious, scary, surprising or problem-solving; the aim is to have fun together.

Helping your child to change

Perhaps your child has a bad habit you would like to cure or a problem to solve. It is surprisingly easy to change habits by following this sequence:

1. Choose your goal. You already know what you don't want. It might be whingeing or not obeying until the 15th time you ask, for instance. The first step is to turn this around and specify what you do want.

For   whingeing...use a normal voice
        not obeying...do it straight away
        hitting...use words to let people know you're angry
        being a loner...join in the game

2. Consider possible reasons for the behaviour. You could ask the child for *their* reasons but they may not know. Also, think over any changes or circumstances which could have triggered the problem. A child might be disobedient because they have a hearing impairment. Perhaps they are allergic to food dye or farm sprays in your area.

3. Decide to act. Explain to the child the new rules — what will be happening from now on and your goal. Be strong and stick to your decisions.

4. Look at yourself as an example to your child. Sometimes we have to fix the problem in ourselves first. If we solve problems by hitting our child, we can hardly expect them not to hit, too. If we don't go out and make friends, we can't expect them to be good at socialising.

5. Be creative — try new options. Don't brutalise children if they don't respond. Sometimes it takes time to find out there is something beyond their control. Check that the new goal is within their ability — appropriate to their age and physically possible for them. (Remember that if a child has done a thing properly once, it *is* within their ability.) Once you've decided that it's an appropriate goal, get in and help them to *want* to do it. Creativity can give you amazing solutions and make parenting a lot more fun.

6. Be positive. Look for and reward each success. Keep imagining your child as having already achieved the goal. Say encouraging things like: 'I know you are good at playing with other kids. Go and ask if you can join in.' 'You are very clever at working things out. Go and try again.' 'You got the first part right — you picked up your toys and took them to your room. Now you have to think about the right place to put them.'

Here are a couple of solutions from parents:

● Regan, 7, had to be asked nine times before he would do what he was told. His mother decided she would double the amount of work she was giving him, instead of just repeating her request. His reactions speeded up wonderfully.

● Elly, 6, was dreamy, so her mother clapped her hands in front of the child's face, then asked: 'What did I just say to you, Elly?' That got her attention straight away.

The parenting group had a tea break...and a toilet break, after talking to Harry and Marg about their son's bladder!

The next questioner was Jane, who had astonished the group by saying she had five children under eight years of age, yet was still able to smile and speak coherently.

I've got one who whinges. She really gets me down.

What do you want instead?

I want her to not do it.

Not talk? Or not whinge?

(Jane laughed.)

Would you like it if she used a normal voice?

Yes.

Why do you think she whinges?

Well, I'm pretty busy with the baby. She just goes on and on at me, until I give in for peace.

So, it works.

Yes, I guess it does.

Smart kid.

But annoying. I can't stand to be around her. It gets me down.

Memory improvement

As children get closer to school age, they need to be able to remember what they have been asked to do and to get things in order. For instance: 'Finish your drink, put the cup on the sink, then do your hair.' By using this game as practice, from a very young age, they can build up their confidence and ability to remember a series of instructions, and carry them out independently. Over time, make it harder. The following are approximate ages and what can be taught:

1½ to 2½ 'Go into my bedroom and get my red slippers, please.'

2½ to 3½ 'Go to Daddy in the kitchen and ask what time it is, then come and tell me.'

3½ to 4½ 'Go and see where the big and little hands of the clock are pointing, then come and tell me and I'll tell you what time it is.'

You'll notice that children love to help and can get things for you, and will be proud of remembering. If you are pinned down feeding a baby, your toddler can bring you a biscuit or get a nappy from the shelf, and you will appreciate the help.

There are two reasons for whingeing that we encounter all the time. Firstly, it's the only 'wavelength' that gets through. If the child asks normally, people don't listen. This is common in big or very busy families.

Secondly, the parents use whingeing voices and the child is speaking the family language.

The group was amazed how well Jane had coped with all those children; whingeing was a relatively small problem in the circumstances. Jane and each of her children were probably much in need of individual time together. To get started on solving the problem of helping her daughter to speak pleasantly, Jane was happy to consider these steps:

HOW TO HELP A CHILD TO SPEAK PLEASANTLY

1. Show the child what a normal voice is and how their usual voice sounds.

2. Tell them you will only listen and help them if they use a normal voice.*

*This doesn't mean she will automatically get what she asks for in a normal voice — just that she has a better chance. You can explain: 'You asked for that really well. But you can't have a biscuit because tea is almost ready.'

3. Demonstrate and explain. Practise together a whingeing voice and a normal voice, saying the same words. Make a game of it if you like. (It's really pretty funny.)

4. Take note the next time she uses a pleasant, normal voice and tell her you've noticed.

5. Resolve not to answer questions, nor give her what she wants, unless she asks in a normal voice. Occasional reminders will keep her on track.

The interesting thing is that a child's whole personality can change once they change voices. How you sound affects how you feel. If you speak more evenly, you feel better, and if you don't sound like a victim, you won't be one.

It was getting dark outside when the parenting course ended for the day. We were amazed when we thought about how much goes into making four-year-olds what they are, and how much learning and growing they do at that tender age. As leaders of the course, we felt comfortable that, while we had offered some clarity, it was the collective wisdom and sheer warmth and friendliness of these parents towards each other that would help them with their families, as they headed off into the night to be with them again.

Preparing for school

Much sooner than you expected, your child is approaching the age of five and it's time to start thinking about school. Everything you have done with your child up to this age has helped them to become 'school ready'. They will already have mastered, or be well on the way to mastering, such 'school-useful' skills as:

● Recognising and perhaps writing their name.

● Concentrating for reasonable lengths of time (this helps with listening to stories and carrying out activities in the classroom).

● Knowing how to go to the toilet and wash their hands.

● Knowing to wait when an adult is busy talking to someone else, then taking their turn to speak (this takes lots of practice and reminders).

● Recognising what they are feeling and knowing how to use words to ask for what they want.

● Knowing their parents' names and their home address.

● Knowing to stay away from strangers, the road and busy traffic.

● Putting on a hat before going outside to play.

● Knowing the importance of not hurting other people or themselves.

● Some fine motor skills, such as cutting, pasting, drawing, writing, threading, building with blocks and so on, and some gross motor skills, including running, jumping, hopping, skipping and climbing. They will be good at a number of these and only just learning others.

They will have had opportunities to play with children of their own age and will have some experience of sharing, being friendly and enjoying time with others. Also, they will, hopefully, be able to follow the teacher's instructions. Don't expect the teacher to have a magic wand; if you can't get them to obey, the teacher may not be able to, either. Even highly skilled and caring teachers need children to meet them halfway by being 'teachable'.

Ideally, a child of school age should have already spent some time in other people's homes or in the care of trusted adults other than their parents. This way, they will have had the chance to get used to being in a new place without you and to know that you can be relied on to return.

Familiarisation with the school
You and your child need to feel comfortable with the school, so check it out as follows:

Children enjoying group activities — a sign that they are ready for school. Playgroups are inexpensive and found everywhere — and if your neighbourhood doesn't have one you can get help to start one yourself.

Enjoying visits to the doctor and dentist

Your child can become familiar and comfortable with these visits by seeing you being examined by a doctor and having your teeth checked by a dentist. Wait until they are old enough to ask questions (approximately two years plus) or take another adult along to mind the child. Preferably, don't start when you are having wisdom teeth removed — something easy would be best.

Before you go, explain simply what is going to happen. If you like, you can ring the receptionist beforehand or ask when you arrive if your child can watch and learn. For some parents, this is challenging. Some find it hard enough to relax and cope with the dentist's drills and injections or to feel comfortable with the intimacy of a doctor performing a physical examination. Surprisingly, though, we can often teach ourselves to be more calm, positive and relaxed, when we are busy putting on a show to reassure our child.

Many dentists and doctors are friendly and interested in children, and know the benefits of having a child who feels at ease. Dentists even let children sit in the chair and show them the 'magic' toothbrushes which tickle their fingers. They are getting to know a familiar face and name, have seen and tried some of the equipment and, importantly, have heard the noises and smelt the smells in an atmosphere of adventure and interest. If more of us had this beginning, we would be happier patients.

Soon, your child will be saying: 'I want to see Dr Stone, he'll make my ache better' or: 'I like Mal, he's my best dentist.'

Sue, 26 'I was on my way to the doctor for a breast examination and was trying to think how to explain this to my three-year-old because he wants to know about everything. So I said: "The doctor wants to check parts of my body to see if they are all working well" and I told him he'd probably look at my eyes, ears, chest, heart and breasts. In the waiting room, my son said, in a very loud voice, "Mummy, is doctor going to feel your breasts?" I said: "Yes, now where are the blocks?", trying to distract him and hoping the other patients hadn't really heard. But it got worse. "Does doctor like to feel your breasts, Mummy?" Well, they heard that time!'

● Do the kids look happy and play well, or are there angry-looking cliques or a lack of spontaneous, happy play?
● Are the staff reasonably relaxed or are they over-worked and under-appreciated?
● Does the school have reasonable standards of cleanliness and safety, such as boundary fences?
● What do other parents think of the school?
● Ask to meet your child's teacher.
● Go back to the school a couple of times, so that you both get used to the physical setting, size, smell, sounds.
● Allow your child to go inside the toilet block.
● Take them on a boundary walk, so they can look back to see the position of the classrooms from different angles.
● Let them play on the equipment — it's a big drawcard!
● Help your child to rehearse the teacher's name.
● It certainly helps to have a friend to start school with.
● If you are new to the area, ask the principal to suggest a local family with whom you could make contact, then the kids could meet before school begins.

Remember that if you are confident and enthusiastic about your child going to school, it is highly likely they will feel good about it, too.

Cause for celebration

The first day of school is one to celebrate, so plan something special as a gift to yourselves, the parents. This is an important milestone. You have spent thousands of hours caring, guiding and helping, thinking about and working for this five-year-old who is now launched into their school years. Congratulations.

Clare, 26 'We had saved up for this day, keeping all the £1 coins from our change in a jar. And, on the last day of the first week our daughter was at school, Max and I went out for a champagne lunch. I'd never done anything so extravagant and it felt like total luxury. We talked over the good times and what had seemed like major problems which had now faded away. We realised a lot of parenting lay ahead, but we had reached a big milestone. We had done it together. The day was a great memory to keep for both of us.'

Helping to build motor skills

These ideas were collated by the specialist teacher at our local school, Mrs Robbie Poynter. Use them in a fun way, without pressure, and your child is sure to enjoy them and come back for more.

1. Tie a balloon to a fairly short piece of string. Hold on to the end of the string and bat the inflated balloon back and forth with your hand. Extend the length of string, hit back and forth to a partner, without letting it touch the floor.

2. Put pegs around an (empty) ice-cream container or old tin with thin, smooth edge. How many can you peg on your clothes? Help Mum peg out the washing, doll's or teddy bear's clothes.

3. Tidy Mum's sewing basket. Rewind the cottons and roll up the wool. Make pom-poms (big, small, rainbow, for hats, clown noses and buttons). Sew buttons on to strips of material. Draw pictures on to cardboard, punch holes and sew around.

4. Suspend a tennis ball on elastic from a tree limb, verandah or monkey bar, and practise hitting with a cheap, light bat.

5. Play with a yoyo, winding up the string, dropping and returning yoyo to hand.

6. Play hand soccer by rolling a tennis ball around the floor, aiming between two objects, like tins or mugs, for goals. Toss ball from hand to hand. Pass the ball from hand to hand around tummy, legs and then in reverse direction.

7. Play tiddly winks. Aim into saucer, bowl, cup.

8. Roll marbles. Push, drop down pipes and tubes.

9. Bounce a tennis ball and catch it in a small container.

10. Hammer nails.

11. Thread buttons.

12. Knit.

13. Build with Lego, manipulative toys, nuts and bolts.

14. Decorate cakes with sultanas, small pieces of chocolate, silver cachous.

15. Fold paper — origami and paper planes.

16. Dismantle old appliances to see how they work (watch your telephone and TV set!). Get some old phones from Telecom, record players and so on. Pull them to bits — unscrew, unwind, twist off. It's amazing how many parts make up a telephone.

17. Plant seeds and flowers.

Harmony and happiness

How can parents nurture their child's spiritual development? Here are some ways in which we help our children (and ourselves) to appreciate the fullness of life:

Compassion

This means considering the feelings of other people and living things. By thinking this way, one is able to act with kindness arising from empathy. Little children have lots of natural compassion — they hate to see an animal hurting or a younger child crying, for instance. You can help strengthen compassion by teaching them how to notice the feelings of others and to show gentleness towards insects, animals and so on. When they show small acts of kindness, comment on them. And, of course, treat your children kindly, so that they experience the feeling of receiving care.

Harmony with nature

Enjoy the outdoors together. Watch the sunrise or, at night, go into the countryside to hear and see the animals. Sit quietly in wild places. Go camping. Grow plants.

Recycle. Encourage tidiness and cleanliness, and point out the pleasures of clean sheets on the bed, clean clothes on their skin.

Optimism

Talk about the beauty and happiness around us. Strictly limit TV watching and computer games. Children under five should not have to see the images and hear the messages on TV or radio news, for instance. They are able to understand, but cannot appreciate the context of these things and will get a frightening and distorted view of the world. This can lead to behaviour problems, such as aggression, as they try to cope with their inner fears.

This isn't a matter of painting a false picture; the world *is* largely positive, with a majority of safe, trustworthy people. There are real problems in the world, but worrying about them is adults' work, not little children's. When you discuss problems, talk about what *you*, as a family, can do about them. Concepts which you want them to take on, such as 'there is some good in everyone', 'things have a way of working out' and 'for every problem there is a solution', can be mentioned quietly and will become part of their attitude.

Forgiveness and problem solving

Self esteem and confidence come not from being perfect, but from being able to take a mistake or setback and *think* your way around it. Children can learn to think and feel at the same time, and take responsibility for their actions, without having to cover up mistakes or not try for fear of failure. You can say, 'Well, that was a mistake, but I'm sure you can fix it up.' When a problem arises, help them with brainstorming possible solutions, trying things to see if they work and trying again if they don't. This will give your children a 'can do' approach to life which will become part of their character forever.

Peacefulness

Encourage concentration, by allowing children to play uninterrupted and absorb themselves in learning. Have a quiet house, at least some of the time. Teach your children relaxation through stories, tapes and by giving them a massage.

Open-mindedness

● All people matter. You can demonstrate this by always greeting your children by name and saying goodbye individually. They, in turn, say 'hello', adding the person's name if they know it, and 'good morning' and 'good night' to each person in the home.

● All points of view matter. Don't put down people, groups, religions or races in front of your children. Point out that ideas and beliefs change. They might believe one way now and another later. In answer to questions, tell them, 'Some people believe... while others think...' When they

ask you for an answer, don't always give them your views. Ask them what they think and why.

Appreciating differences

Where possible, expose your children naturally and easily to people of different ages, abilities, handicaps, races and talents. Talk about your own 'disabilities', so they realise that these are normal and surmountable. As they are growing up, show them that you value people of different races, cultures, beliefs, sexual preferences and so on.

Self-acceptance

This quality arises out of being accepted unconditionally in one's family. If you have experienced acceptance as a child, you will go into the world expecting it and usually getting it, because you radiate this assurance. Give loving messages clearly and unambiguously: 'I'm glad you are here in this family; it's great to have you around.'

Of course, you will criticise and seek to change behaviour, but always separate this from the person. 'I don't like what you are doing.' You can even put compliments into your criticisms. 'You are far smarter than that. I know you can think of a better way to solve the argument. Let's see you do it.'

Wellness

Expect and help children to take care of their bodies, because they are important and valuable. Talk about how their bodies are strong and well, and how they have lots of energy. Point out how good children are at healing quickly. Place high value on their diet, exercise and safety, such as always fastening their seatbelts in the car. This all says, 'You are precious.'

Happiness

Help children to value others' happiness as well as their own. 'Look how happy Jenni is with the present you gave her.' 'I like being with you, you are really good fun.' We all aim to give our children a happy childhood, but the eventual message we want them to have is that happiness is a choice.

Point out the ways they know to help themselves feel happy — playing with their favourite toys; inviting other children to play with them; sitting and being peaceful for a while with a book or toy; having a bath and playing in it. We can actively encourage even young children by routinely using statements like: 'Have a happy time', 'enjoy yourself', 'find something you'd like to do.'

Spiritual practices

We adults may have spiritual practices of our own, having discovered how much they help our lives. Some people go to church, others meditate or do yoga; some observe family rituals, follow special diets, gather for study or discussion and so on. It is surprising that, having discovered the benefits, parents can be reluctant to involve their children in these practices. Yet, when it comes to pushing children to do such things as brushing their teeth and picking up their toys, we have no hesitation. Our children may get the feeling that tidiness matters more than spiritual practice.

We believe that children can be encouraged to try, stick with and, as they grow older, find out for themselves the potential benefits of spiritual practices. With some flexibility to accommodate young children's needs, spiritual practices in childhood can remain a positive memory. They also create a 'spiritual space' in a child's mind which, as a teenager and adult, they can build on in their own way. They will know that there is more meaning to life than possessions, approval or outer success and will be hardier and more self-directed.

The above is an abbreviated guide to a huge subject. Perhaps the biggest challenge, when we acknowledge that our children have a need for spiritual guidance from us, is to work out how this is expressed in our lives. Whatever we say to them won't matter as much as what they notice about *our* serenity, *our* compassion, *our* free-spiritedness and *our* happiness in the world. Which is quite a challenge!

Index

Pages numbers in **bold print** refer to main entries

ACKNOWLEDGEMENTS

I sincerely thank all those who offered their stories, living example and personal encouragement, especially:

Iris Johnstone, Cathy Krushka, Bess Gleeson, Jean Bowkett, Valda Donald, Dr John Morris, Elizabeth and Ken Mellor, Val and Robin Maslen, Peter Clarke from *Offspring*, Mary, Christina and Sarah Sharpe, Lindy, Neil, Emma, Sophie and Lewis Shillito, Jenny, Neville, Ben, Luke and Elle Mathewson, Kerry, Ray and Joseph Pickett, Vikki, Franco and Zoe Giarraputo, Collinsvale School staff Ruth Lansdell, Janette Prior, Wendy Cracknell, Maria Hedge, Roberta Poynter, Zelda Probin, Cec Craft, Lee Hodge, Libby Craft, Penny Irving, Dave Pycroft, Dr Ilona Bewsher, Tom and Cynthia Dunbabin, Maureen and Ray Campbell, Adriana and Beres Taylor, Toni Johnstone, Jeni and John Bright, Vicky Sauvage, Chris Cadogan, Dianne Mallett, Sr Helen McKibben, Denise Cook, Sharon Langerak, Claudette Wells, Christine Howard.

The stories and examples in this book have come from our own experience or were reported by friends, teachers, nurses, doctors, social workers and course participants. Identifying details have been altered to protect privacy and some stories are composites of similar or common experiences.

I would love to receive feedback from mothers and fathers who read this book, as well as stories about what has worked for you. Please write to Shaaron Biddulph, c/- Post Office, Collinsvale, Tasmania 7012.

PICTURE CREDITS

The publishers would like to thank the Mater Misericordiae Hospital and Julia Sundin, physiotherapist.

This edition published in 1995 by
Leopard Books
Random House, 20 Vauxhall Bridge Road,
London SW1V 2SA

First published in 1994 by Murdoch Books®,
a division of Murdoch Magazines Pty Ltd

© Murdoch Books®, 1994

© Text: Shaaron and Steve Biddulph
Illustrations: Lorraine Hannay
Cartoons: Richard Collins
Photography: Leigh Clapp, Reg Morrison, Peter Webb

ISBN 0 7529 0085 4

Designer: Leigh Nankervis
Photographers: Leigh Clapp, Reg Morrison, Peter Sledge, Peter Webb
Illustrator: Lorraine Hannay
Cartoonist: Richard Collins

Typeset by Post Typesetters, Brisbane
Produced by Mandarin Offset, Hong Kong

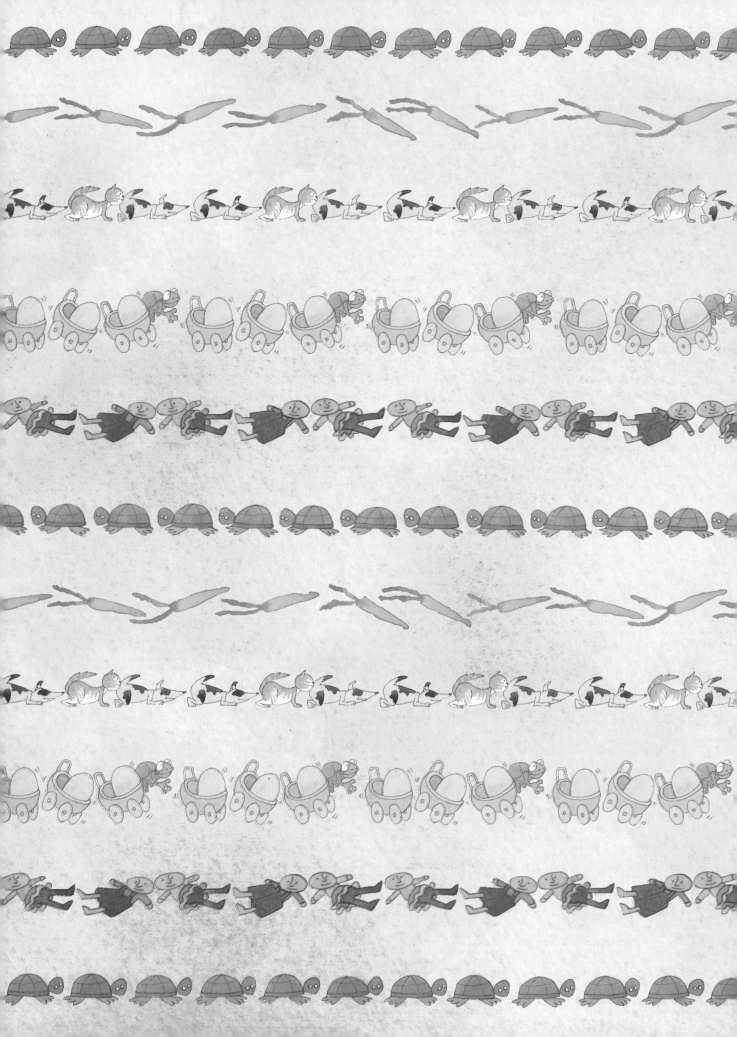